Essential Year 7 Maths practice from CGP!

There's a lot to get your head around in KS3 Maths, but don't worry — this CGP Workbook will help you master anything Year 7 can throw at you.

Each section starts with warm-up questions to make sure you're ready to get started. After that, there's stacks of brilliant practice to build up those vital Maths skills. It's all split into topics, so it's easy to target anything you're finding tough.

And there's more... we've also included plenty of review exercises so you can check how you're doing, plus fully worked answers to every question. Everything you need!

CGP — still the best! ☺

Our sole aim here at CGP is to produce the highest quality books — carefully written, immaculately presented and dangerously close to being funny.

Then we work our socks off to get them out to you — at the cheapest possible prices.

Published by CGP

Editors:
Adam Bartlett, Michael Bushell, Sarah George, Tom Miles, Rosa Roberts, Caley Simpson, Dawn Wright

ISBN: 978 1 78908 316 3

With thanks to Alastair Duncombe, Shaun Harrogate and Glenn Rogers for the proofreading.

Clipart from Corel®
Printed by Elanders Ltd, Newcastle upon Tyne.

Based on the classic CGP style created by Richard Parsons.

Contents

How To Use This Book

- **Hold the book upright, approximately 50 cm from your face, ensuring that the text looks like this, not sᴉɥʇ. Alternatively, place the book on a horizontal surface (e.g. a table or desk) and sit adjacent to the book, at a distance which doesn't make the text too small to read.**
- **In case of emergency, press the two halves of the book together firmly in order to close.**
- **Before attempting to use this book, familiarise yourself with the following safety information:**

Different schools teach Key Stage 3 Maths in a slightly different order. Don't panic if you come across something you haven't learned yet — just skip that topic and move on. If there's a topic missing, you'll probably find it in our Year 8 or Year 9 book. There's a table at the back of this book showing you where everything is covered.

This book has five sections covering different areas of maths. Each section is split up into topics, so it's easy to find questions on a specific thing you want to practise.

Every question in this book has a fully worked solution at the back — the answers start on page 81.

There's plenty of space below each question for you to do your working. Then write your answer on the dotted line.

....

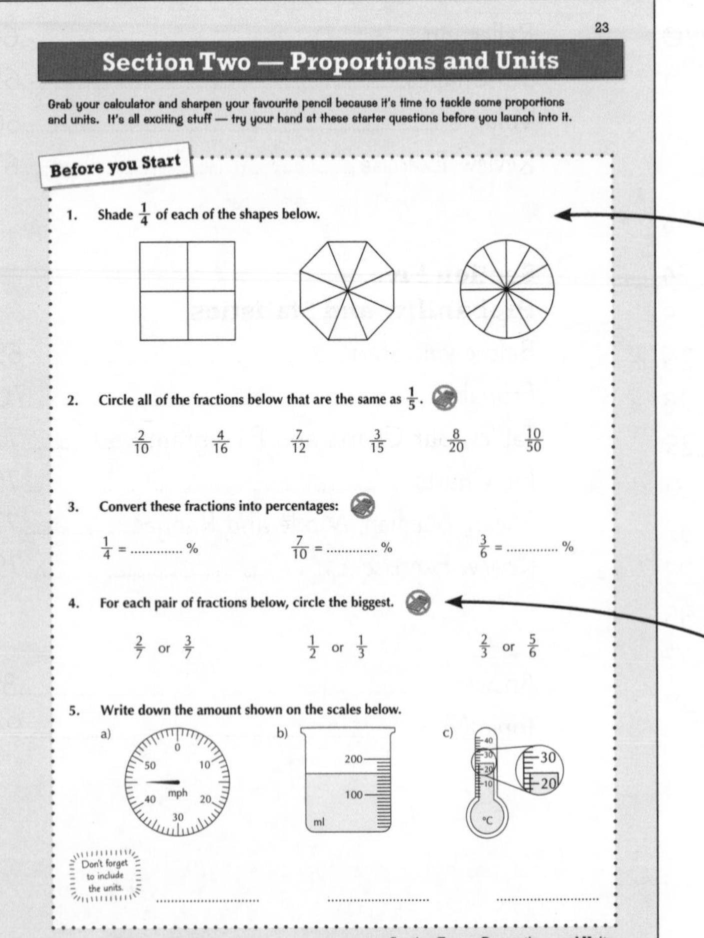

23

Section Two — Proportions and Units

Grab your calculator and sharpen your favourite pencil because it's time to tackle some proportions and units. It's all exciting stuff — try your hand at these starter questions before you launch into it.

Before you Start

1. Shade $\frac{1}{4}$ of each of the shapes below.

2. Circle all of the fractions below that are the same as $\frac{1}{5}$.

$\frac{2}{10}$ $\frac{4}{16}$ $\frac{7}{12}$ $\frac{3}{15}$ $\frac{8}{20}$ $\frac{10}{50}$

3. Convert these fractions into percentages:

$\frac{1}{4}$ = ... % $\frac{7}{10}$ = ... % $\frac{3}{6}$ = ... %

4. For each pair of fractions below, circle the biggest.

$\frac{2}{7}$ or $\frac{3}{7}$ $\frac{1}{2}$ or $\frac{1}{3}$ $\frac{2}{3}$ or $\frac{5}{6}$

5. Write down the amount shown on the scales below.

a) b) c)

Don't forget to include the units.

....

Section Two — Proportions and Units

Each section starts with some quick questions to make sure you know the basics before launching in.

Calculators are useful but you need to be able to solve problems without them too. You'll see questions in this book with this stamp next to them — this means you can't use a calculator for any part of the question. (You'll thank us one day...)

How To Use This Book

Each topic has a page or two of questions that get more challenging as you work through them.

There are some hints to help you answer specific questions.

Questions with blue boxes around the question number are a bit trickier than the others. These questions also test your problem-solving skills — you need to figure out what you have to do for yourself.

Each topic ends with a checklist. Tick off each point when you're happy you can do it. If there's anything you're unsure about, this is a good time to go back and have another look at it.

32

Finding Percentages Using a Calculator

1. Work out the following.

You can either multiply by the equivalent decimal or use your calculator's % button.

18% of 250 .... 4% of 675 .... 162% of 1050 ....

2. Lukas is given £26 for his birthday. He spends 11% of the money on a magazine about kangaroos and donates a further 57% of the money to a koala hospital.

a) How much money did Lukas donate to the hospital?

£ ....

b) How much money does Lukas have left?

£ ....

3. A greengrocer has an offer where customers get 23% extra free on their shopping.

a) Pauline buys 860 g of plums. How many grams of plums does Pauline receive for free?

23% EXTRA FREE

.... g

The sign on the left shows two offers available from a butcher.

12% discount OR £4 off your bill

b) Pauline's bill comes to £37 before either offer is applied. Which offer will save her the most money? Tick your answer.

☐ 12% discount ☐ £4 off your bill

How did you do?

Calculators are allowed on this page and that's always a pleasure. By now, you should be able to:

☐ **Find percentages using a calculator.**

Section Two — Proportions and Units

Tick the box that matches how confident you feel with the topic. This should help to show you where you need to do a bit more practice.

79

Section Five — Review Exercise

So that's Section Five all wrapped up. Well, apart from these review questions, that is. They'll really test if you've got to grips with all that probability and stats. Off you go.

1. A group of teenagers are on a school trip in the countryside. They check the signal strength on their phones and record the number of bars of signal in this pictogram.

Bars of signal	
None	
1	
2	
3	
4+	

Key: = 4 phones

a) How many phones have exactly one bar of signal?

.... 1 mark

b) One of the teenagers is picked at random from the group. Put a cross (X) on this line to mark the probability of this teenager's phone having exactly one bar of signal.

0 0.2 0.4 0.6 0.8 1

1 mark

2. A shoe shop records the shoe size of eight people who visit the shop. The results are shown below.

8 6 10 10 12 9 9 8

a) Find:

(i) the median shoe size,

.... 1 mark

(ii) the mean shoe size.

.... 2 marks

b) A frequency table for all 1056 visitors to the shoe shop in a year is given below.

Shoe size	6	7	8	9	10	11	12
Frequency	174	134	231	253	115	98	51

What fraction of the visitors had a shoe size greater than 9? Give your answer in its simplest form.

.... 2 marks

Section Five — Review Exercise

Once you've made it to the end of a section, have a go at the Review Exercise to test how much you remember. Each exercise has two pages of questions that cover the topics in the section.

Review questions have marks allocated to them — the worked solutions show what you need to do to get each mark.

Section One — Number

This section is all about numbers — there's a fair bit to cover, but I know you're up to the task. Before you get carried away and pull a muscle, here's a collection of easy questions to get you warmed up.

Before you Start

1. **Fill in the gaps to complete the following calculations.** 

   7 + 13 = 5 + ...   12 + 17 = 10 + ...

2. **Complete the following calculations.** 

	1	9
+	3	2
	☐	☐

	6	6
−	4	7
	☐	☐

3. **A number line is drawn below.**

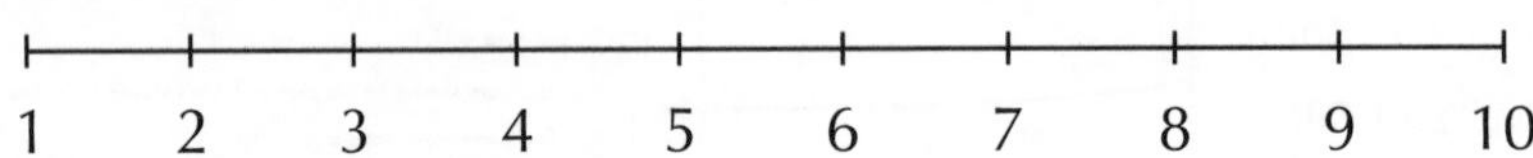

   a) Circle all the even numbers.

   b) Mark with a cross where the number 4.5 should go.

4. **Complete the multiplication table below, then answer the following questions.** 

×	6	7	8	9
6				
7				
8				
9				

   a) What is 54 ÷ 6?

   ....

   b) Write 74 ÷ 8 as a whole number plus a remainder.

   .... remainder ....

5. **A strong gust of wind has blown some numbers off the calculations below. Place the numbers back into their boxes to make the calculations correct.** 

☐ + ☐ = 12

☐ − ☐ = 4

4 6 2 8

Place Value and Ordering Numbers

1. Gary has poked a nest, causing a swarm of angry numbers. Calm the swarm by drawing a circle around every number you see with a 5 in the tens column.

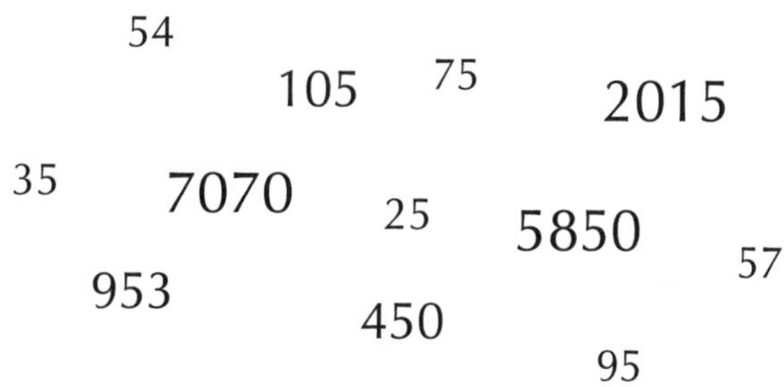

2. Order the following from smallest to largest: 968 ml, 869 ml, 989 ml, 986 ml, 896 ml.

.... ml, ... ml, ... ml, ... ml, ... ml

3. For each pair of numbers below, choose the correct symbol from the shelf to fill the box.

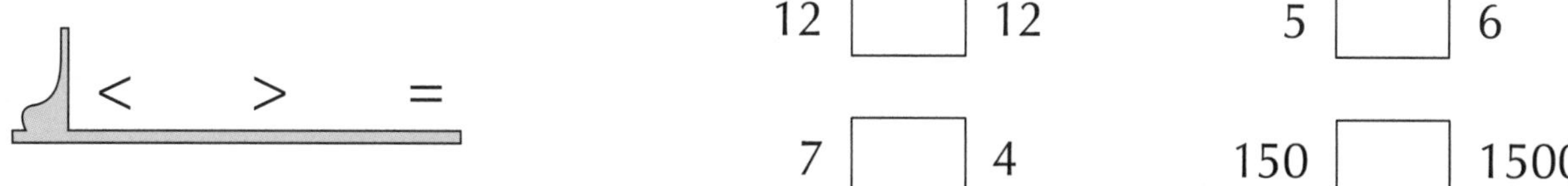

4. The code to my safe is "one million, ninety-eight thousand, four hundred and twelve".

a) Write down this value as a number.

....

b) What is the digit in the ones column?

....

c) What is the digit in the thousands column?

....

How did you do?

That's about it for whole numbers — I hope Gary made it out OK. Before you go, make sure you can:

- ☐ Understand place value in whole numbers.
- ☐ Compare and order whole numbers.
- ☐ Understand and use inequality symbols.

Place Value and Ordering Decimals

1. Circle each number you see with a 3 in the hundredths column.

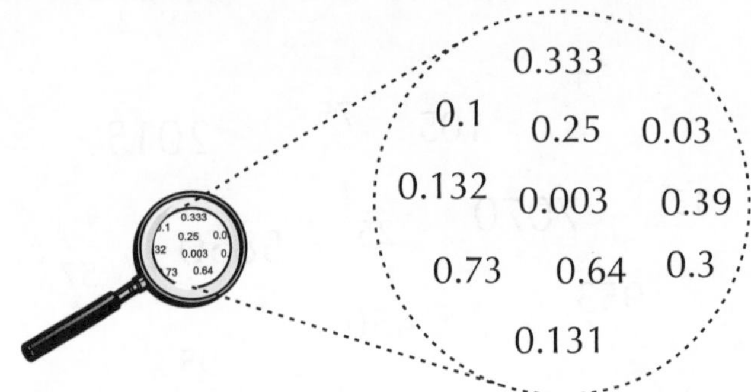

2. Amir has 1.20 litres of yoghurt and Lara has 1.02 litres of yoghurt. Who has more?

....

3. Put the following numbers in order, starting from the smallest.

13.29	13	13.2	13.15	13.3	13.05

....

4. Write down the decimal number described by the following clues.

- The number has two digits after the decimal point, and one digit before the decimal point.
- There's a 0 in the ones column.
- There's a 5 in the hundredths column.
- It's larger than 0.2, but smaller than 0.3.

....

How did you do?

You'll probably agree, decimals are trickier than whole numbers — that little decimal point can be a bit of a nuisance. If you've made it this far you're ready to move on, but first make sure you can:

☐ **Understand place value in decimal numbers.** ☐ **Compare and order decimal numbers.**

Adding and Subtracting Whole Numbers

1. 
Complete the following calculations. 

```
    2  5  4         1  □  6         4  5  7         9  1  2
+   3  4  7     +   4  7  5     -   2  6  1     -   3  □  □
   ________        ________        ________        ________
    □  □  □         □  3  □         □  □  □         □  7  7
```

2. Sasha adds two numbers on her calculator and gets the result shown below. 

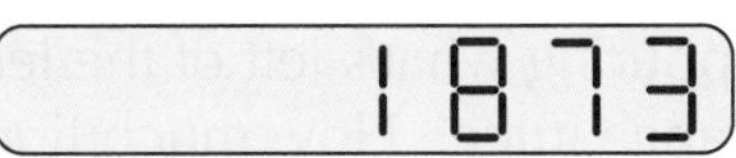

One of the numbers was 796. What was the other number?

....

3. The table below shows the number of pupils in each tutor group at a school. 

	Group M	Group A	Group T	Group H	Group S
No. of pupils	14	19	18	17	16

During school assemblies, groups M, T and H sit on the left-hand side of the hall, and groups A and S sit on the right-hand side.

a) How many pupils sit on the left-hand side of the hall?

....

b) Including teachers, there are 97 people in the hall. How many teachers are there?

....

How did you do?

There's no avoiding addition and subtraction — they're pretty vital mathematical skills. Before I let you go, I'll need you to tick the boxes and sign your name on the dotted line.

☐ I confirm I can add whole numbers. ☐ I confirm I can subtract whole numbers.

☐ I confirm I didn't use a calculator. Signed ....

Adding and Subtracting Decimals

1. Work out these calculations.

1.5 + 2.3 = ... 4.5 – 3.2 = ...

2. Beth has a 330 ml can of sugar-free lemonade.
She takes a gulp and drinks 20.4 ml from the can.

a) How much lemonade is left in the can?

.... ml

b) Beth makes a mocktail by pouring what's left of the lemonade into a glass that contains 43.3 ml of orange juice. How much liquid is in the glass?

.... ml

3. Nicky has £4.50 and Sally has 70p.

a) Sally wants to buy a newspaper costing £1.30. How much more money does she need?

£...............

b) Nicky lends Sally the money she needs to buy the newspaper, then spends £1.80 on a magazine. How much money does Nicky have left?

£...............

4. An airline allows each passenger three bags with a total mass of no more than 20 kg.

Can I fly with bags weighing 5.31 kg, 6.483 kg and 8.159 kg? Explain your answer.

How did you do?

You can add and subtract decimals just like whole numbers, but make sure you line up the decimal points. You've had quite the decimal workout on this page — by now you should be able to:

☐ **Add and subtract decimal numbers.**

Multiplying & Dividing by 10, 100, 1000 etc.

1. Draw a line to connect each number on the left to a number on the right.
Each line represents 'multiplying by 100'. I've drawn the first one to help you.

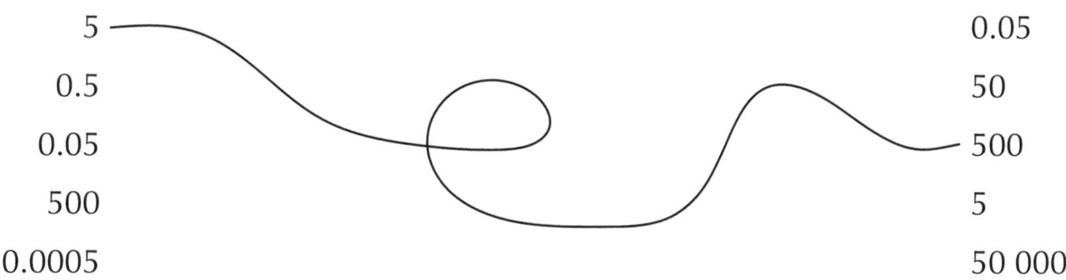

2. Work out the following calculations.

1.8 ÷ 10 = ...   0.12 ÷ 100 = ...   41 500 ÷ 10 000 = ...

3. Choose the correct symbol, '×' or '÷', to fill in the boxes below.

0.4 ☐ 100 = 0.004   0.0076 ☐ 1000 = 7.6   0.3 ☐ 10 = 0.03

4. Fill in the boxes with 10, 100 or 1000.

0.68 × ☐ = 68   5200 ÷ ☐ = 5.2   ☐ × 0.007 = 0.7

5. A balloon has a mass of 0.012 kg.
What is the mass of 100 of these balloons?

.... kg

How did you do?

Multiplying and dividing by a power of ten is all about moving the decimal point by the right number of places in the right direction. By now, you should be able to:

☐ Multiply by 10, 100, 1000, etc.   ☐ Divide by 10, 100, 1000, etc.

Written Multiplication

1. Complete the following calculations.

43 × 76 .... 75 × 98 .... 732 × 54 ....

2. A bus holds 33 seated passengers.

a) How many seated passengers fit onto 27 buses?

....

b) Each bus also has space for 2 passengers in wheelchairs and 17 passengers standing. How many passengers in total fit onto 27 buses?

....

3. Simone has 3 pet guinea pigs that each eat 60 g of kale a week. How much kale in total do the guinea pigs eat in one year?

1 year = 52 weeks

.... g

How did you do?

You might know a few methods of multiplying numbers — so just stick with the one you're most comfortable with. Whichever method you pick, you should be able to:

☐ Multiply whole numbers.

Written Division

1. Complete the following calculations.

603 ÷ 9

....

576 ÷ 12

....

828 ÷ 36

....

2. Colin's chickens have laid a total of 376 eggs.

a) An egg carton holds 6 eggs. How many egg cartons can Colin fill?

....

b) How many eggs will be left over?

....

3. Thirteen concert tickets cost £767 in total. How much is one ticket?

£...............

4. Work out these divisions. Answer with a whole number and a remainder.

270 ÷ 8

.... remainder ....

410 ÷ 18

.... remainder ....

5. A factory produces 4992 playing cards every hour. How many whole packs of cards is this?

1 pack = 52 cards

.... packs

How did you do?

Whether you're using short or long division, make sure that you can:

☐ Divide one whole number by another.

☐ Work out a division with a remainder.

Negative Numbers

1. Some numbers are missing from the number line below.

Mark on the numbers –2, –6 and –9.

–10 ... –5 ... 0

2. Order these numbers from lowest to highest.

–11 2 –6 –4 10 4

....

3. Work out the following calculations.

6 + –2 = ... –3 – 7 = ... –1 – –5 = ... –4 + –7 = ...

4. Answer true (☑) or false (☒) to the following statements.

$-2 < -5$ ☐ $-4 \geq -6$ ☐ $-7 \leq -10$ ☐ $-8 > -3$ ☐

5. Edward is playing a game of 'Perfect 10'.
To win the game he must throw 3 darts and score exactly 10.

a) His first attempt is shown on the right.
Did Edward win? Explain your answer.

....

....

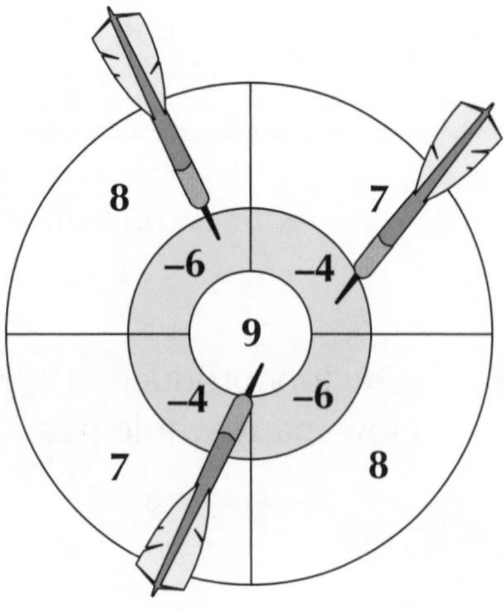

b) If Edward is allowed to throw one of his darts again to get a new score, is it possible for him to win the game? Explain your answer.

....

....

How did you do?

For a tricky subject like this, I'd usually say something about staying positive. But perhaps that's not the best advice for negative numbers. Before you go on, check that you can:

☐ Compare and order negative numbers.

☐ Add and subtract negative numbers.

 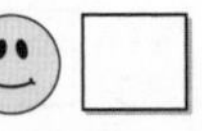 

BODMAS

1. Work out these calculations. 

Use BODMAS to help you remember which order to do the calculations in.

a) $6 + 8 \div 4 - 2$

....

b) $2 \times 3 - 9 \div 3$

....

2. Mila starts with the number 4. She adds 5 to it, then doubles the result. Finally, she subtracts 3. What calculation has she done? Circle your answer.

$4 + 5 \times 2 - 3$ $\quad$ $(4 + 5) \times 2 - 3$ $\quad$ $4 + 5 \times (2 - 3)$ $\quad$ $4 + (5 \times 2) - 3$

3. Add brackets to make each of the following calculations correct. 

a) $1 + 3 \times 2 = 8$

b) $8 - 2 + 1 = 5$

c) $12 \div 3 + 1 = 3$

d) $4 + 2 \times 3 + 1 = 24$

4. Use the tiles on the right to make the number given. Each one tells you the number of tiles to use. 

Tiles: 3, 3, ×, 3,), +, –, (, 3

E.g. Make 18, using 7 tiles:  3 × (3 + 3) $= 3 \times (3 + 3) = 18$.

a) Make 6, using 3 tiles. ....

b) Make –3, using 7 tiles. ....

c) Make 3, using 9 tiles. ....

How did you do?

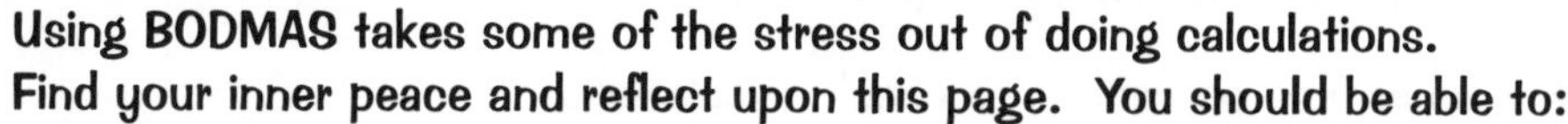

Using BODMAS takes some of the stress out of doing calculations.
Find your inner peace and reflect upon this page. You should be able to:

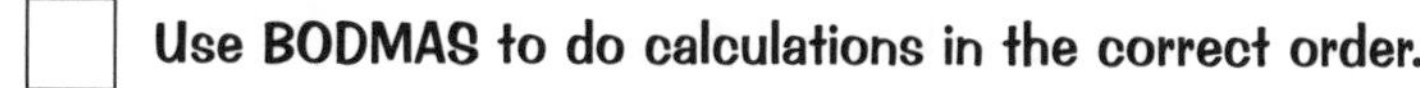

☐ Use BODMAS to do calculations in the correct order.

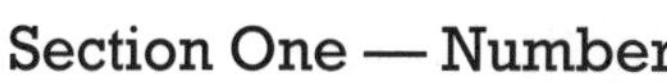

Inverse Operations

1. Tina calculates that 24 + 15 = 39. Fill in the box below to complete a calculation that can be used to check her answer.

39 ☐ 15 = 24

2. Mai calculates that 15 × 4 = 60. What calculation could you do to check her answer?

....

3. For each calculation on the left, there's one on the right that can be used to check the answer.

Match the calculations by drawing straight lines between them.

167 + 252 = 419	337 – 85
252 – 167 = 85	419 – 167
252 + 85 = 337	167 + 85
419 – 85 = 334	85 + 334

4. What is 1795 × 1034 ÷ 1034?

....

5. For each calculation below, use an inverse calculation to show that it's wrong.

a) 125 ÷ 4 = 25

....

b) 7 × 18 = 140

....

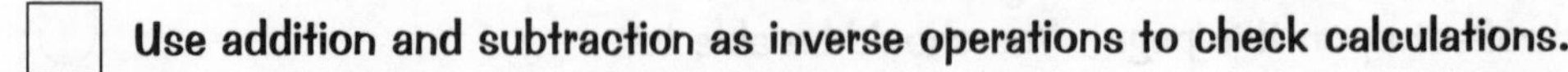

How did you do?

Inverse operations are mathematical 'undos' — one thing undoes another thing to get back to where you started. If you've got that down, you should be able to:

☐ Use addition and subtraction as inverse operations to check calculations.

☐ Use multiplication and division as inverse operations to check calculations.

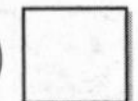  

Rounding

1. Look at Jo's shopping list on the right. Round each item to the nearest ten to help Jo work out how much she'll spend.

13 protractors
28 rulers
165 staples
131 inflatable globes

.... protractors .... rulers

.... staples .... inflatable globes

2. Round each of the following decimals to the nearest whole number.

5.4 rounds to .... 3.8 rounds to .... 14.3 rounds to ....

3. Jasmin is 148.7 cm tall. What is Jasmin's height to the nearest cm?

.... cm

4. Fill in the gaps with '10', '100' or '1000'.

145 = 100 to the nearest ....

12 479 = 12 000 to the nearest ....

129 = 130 to the nearest ....

40 009 = 40 010 to the nearest ....

5. Peter counts the number of apples that he sees growing on a tree. He then rounds this number to the nearest ten. The result is 30.

a) Is it possible that Peter counted exactly 27 apples? Explain your answer.

....

....

b) What is the smallest number of apples that Peter could have counted? Explain your answer.

Think about which numbers round to 30 to the nearest ten.

....

....

How did you do?

Always check what you're rounding to and you'll be a well-rounded mathematician.
Before you go on to the next page, make sure that you can:

- ☐ Round numbers to the nearest whole number.
- ☐ Round numbers to the nearest ten.
- ☐ Round numbers to the nearest hundred.
- ☐ Round numbers to the nearest thousand.

Estimating

1. Cal spent the weekend birdwatching. They saw 36 sparrows, 13 magpies, 24 chaffinches and 8 jackdaws. By rounding each number to the nearest ten, estimate the total number of birds that Cal saw.

....

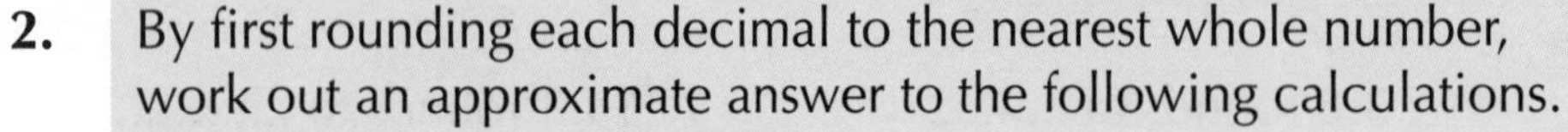

2. By first rounding each decimal to the nearest whole number, work out an approximate answer to the following calculations.

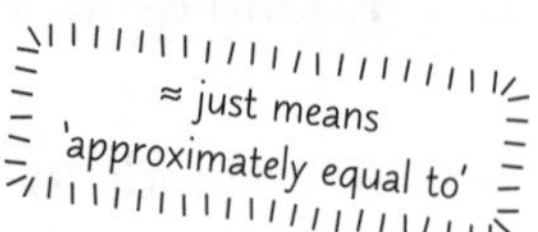

24.2 – 11.9 ≈ .... – .... = ...   9.8 – 15.3 ≈ .... – .... = ...

3. By first rounding each number to the nearest ten, work out an approximate answer to the following calculations.

32 × 17 ≈ .... × .... = ...   98 × 154 ≈ .... × .... = ...

4. A book has a total of 212 pages and 44 031 words. By rounding each number to the nearest hundred, estimate the number of words per page in the book.

....

5. Jason, who's always up for a challenge, attempts to calculate 973 × 432. After a bit of huffing and puffing, he gets an answer of 4 203 036.

a) By rounding each figure to the nearest hundred, estimate the answer to his calculation.

....

b) Do you think Jason has made a mistake in his calculation? Explain your answer.

....

....

How did you do?

So that's it for estimating — it's all about making a calculation easier to deal with, and who wouldn't want that? By now, you should be able to:

☐ **Round numbers to find an estimate to a calculation.**

Powers and Roots

1. Here's a hands-on exercise about square numbers. 

a) Arrange the following pieces into a square. Draw it in the space below.

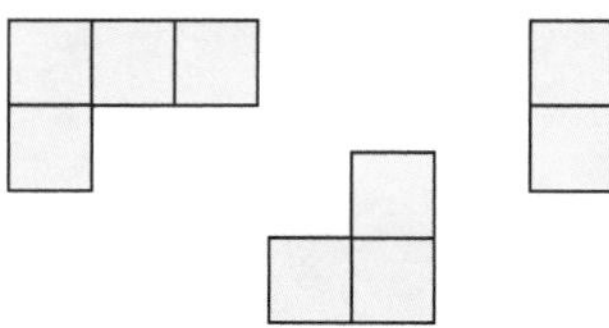

b) Complete the following calculation.

3^2 = ... × .... = ...

c) Explain how your answer to part b) relates to the square from part a).

....

2. Some naughty numbers have been locked behind bars.

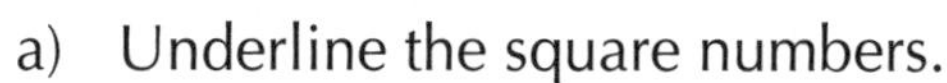

a) Underline the square numbers.

b) Put a circle around every cube number.

4	27	32	25	8
6	36	18	16	3
5	52	64	49	7

3. Rohan buys 64 m² of carpet to fit a square room. What is the width of the room? 

.... m

4. Work out the following. 

$\sqrt[3]{8}$ = ... $\sqrt{81}$ = ... 5^3 = ... $\sqrt[3]{216}$ = ...

How did you do?

Squares, cubes and plants — you'll find roots everywhere you look. For now, your time with powers and roots has come to an end — so check that you can:

- ☐ Calculate squares.
- ☐ Calculate cubes.
- ☐ Calculate square roots.
- ☐ Calculate cube roots.

Multiples and LCM

1. Tick the box next to the sentence A, B or C which describes the numbers: 20, 30, 5, 15, 25.

A: They are all multiples of 2. ☐

B: They are all multiples of 3. ☐

C: They are all multiples of 5. ☐

2. Every multiple of 6 has been circled on the number line below.

1 2 3 4 5 (6) 7 8 9 10 11 (12) 13 14 15 16 17 (18)

a) Circle every multiple of 3 on the number line below.

1 2 3 4 5 6 7 8 9 10 11 12 13 14 15 16 17 18

b) Circle every multiple of 4 on the number line below.

1 2 3 4 5 6 7 8 9 10 11 12 13 14 15 16 17 18

c) What is the lowest common multiple of 3, 4 and 6?

....

3. Rami and Elle are running laps of a track. They set off together.

In this question, each person runs each of their laps in the same time.

a) Rami takes 6 minutes and Elle takes 8 minutes to run a lap.
After how long will they first cross the line together?

.... minutes

b) Omar starts running as Rami and Elle cross the line. It takes 2 hours for all three to cross the line together again. What is the shortest possible time that Omar takes to run a lap?

.... minutes

How did you do?

Well, that's your lot — you'll be glad to know there aren't multiple pages of this stuff. You know the drill by now — check your answers and make sure you can:

☐ **Find multiples of a number.**

☐ **Find common multiples.**

☐ **Find the lowest common multiple of two or three numbers.**

Factors and HCF

1. The factors of 15 are 1, 3, 5 and 15.

a) What are the factors of 18?

.........., ..., ..., ..., ... and ....

b) What are the common factors of 15 and 18?

.... and ....

2. Matt has the following sweets: 10 chocolate bars, 30 lollipops and 70 gummy bears.

a) What are the common factors of 10, 30 and 70?

.........., ..., ... and ....

b) Matt shares the sweets equally into party bags, so that each bag has the same number of each type of sweet. He makes as many party bags as possible.

(i) How many party bags does Matt make?

.... party bags

(ii) How many of each sweet is in each party bag?

.... chocolate bar(s), ... lollipop(s) and .... gummy bear(s)

3. Polly is finding common factors.

a) Write down all the factors of the following numbers.

(i) 60 ....

(ii) 84 ....

b) What is the highest common factor of 60, 84 and 140?

....

How did you do?

Finding factors can be hard work, so you've done well to make it this far.
Here are the things that you should be able to do:

☐ Find factors of a number.

☐ Find common factors.

☐ Find the highest common factor of two or three numbers.

Prime Numbers

1. Circle the numbers in the box that are prime.

21   22   23   27   28   29

2. Explain why 49 is not a prime number.

....

3. The grid on the right shows numbers from 2 to 21.

2	3	4	5	6
7	8	9	10	11
12	13	14	15	16
17	18	19	20	21

a) Follow these instructions:
- Put a cross through all multiples of 2.
- Put a cross through all multiples of 3.
- Put a cross through all multiples of 5.

b) Write down the numbers that haven't been crossed out.

....

c) (i) Is every number listed in b) a prime number? Explain your answer.

....

(ii) Is every prime number less than 21 listed in b)? Explain your answer.

....

4. Put a tick next to each statement that is true.

- [ ] 2 is the only even prime number.
- [ ] All numbers ending in 3 are prime.
- [ ] There is only one prime number ending in 5.
- [ ] There are no prime numbers greater than 100.

How did you do?

There are prizes on offer for finding big prime numbers — they're surprisingly useful. For now though, award yourself a pat on the back and then check you are able to:

- [ ] **Find prime numbers.**
- [ ] **Show when a number is not prime.**

Section One — Review Exercise

It's time to test your knowledge of all things number-related that have been covered in this section. You'll find out what you're best at and what things might need a little more work.

1. Look at the number on the right. 1 4 5 0 3

a) (i) What digit is in the thousands column? ....

(ii) Which column is the digit 5 in? ....

2 marks

b) (i) Divide the number by 10 000.

....

1 mark

(ii) What is the digit in the tenths column of your answer?

....

1 mark

c) Round the original number to the nearest ten.

....

1 mark

2. Work out the following calculations.

a) 2189 + 847 ....

b) 624.1 – 33.59 ....

c) 5435 × 63 ....

d) 2193 ÷ 51 ....

4 marks

3. The temperature is 1 °C and then drops by 3 °C. What is the temperature now?

.... °C

1 mark

4. Work out 7 – 10 ÷ 2 + (–4 + 2).

....

1 mark

5. Leroy has calculated 19 × 87 = 1653.

a) By first rounding each figure to the nearest ten, work out an estimate to 19 × 87.

....

1 mark

b) What calculation could Leroy do to check his answer?

....

1 mark

Section One — Review Exercise

6. a) Which number is bigger: 2^3 or 3^2?

.... 1 mark

b) What is the square root of $3^2 + 4^2$?

.... 1 mark

7. Sandy has three stacks of boxes and each stack is the same height. The first is made up of boxes 20 cm high, the second is made up of boxes 30 cm high and the third is made up of boxes 40 cm high. What is the smallest possible height of a stack?

.... cm 1 mark

8. Zaynab is preparing snack boxes. She has 12 pineapple slices, 20 green olives and 28 carrot sticks to put in the boxes.

a) What are the common factors of 12, 20 and 28?

.........., ... and .... 1 mark

b) If each snack box must have the same amount of each type of food, what is the largest number of snack boxes that Zaynab can make if she wants to use all of the food? Explain your answer.

....

....

2 marks

9. Draw a route through the maze below that passes through only prime numbers.

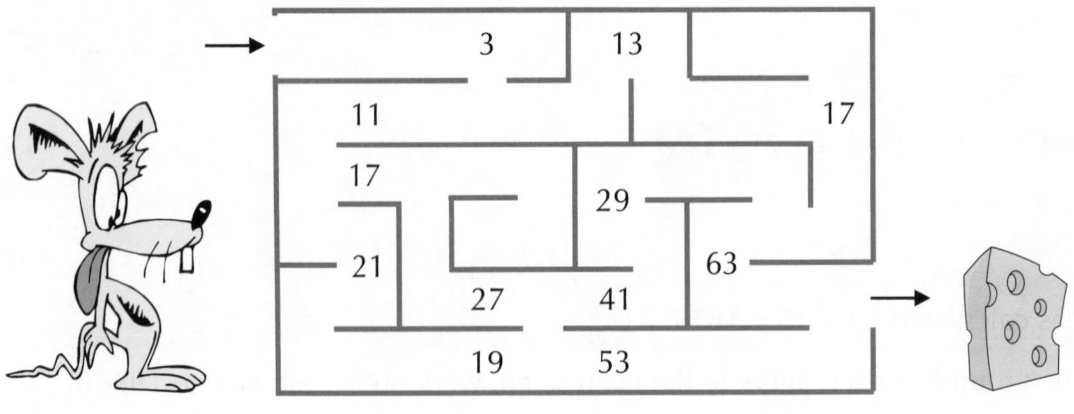

2 marks

I can tell you're in your prime after that amazing performance...

Go ahead and tot up your final score — anything less than full marks only means there's room for improvement. At least you're not still stuck in that maze. Take a breather, then look at the questions where any marks were lost — these will tell you the topics that could do with a bit of studying.

Score: /21

Section Two — Proportions and Units

Grab your calculator and sharpen your favourite pencil because it's time to tackle some proportions and units. It's all exciting stuff — try your hand at these starter questions before you launch into it.

Before you Start

1. Shade $\frac{1}{4}$ of each of the shapes below.

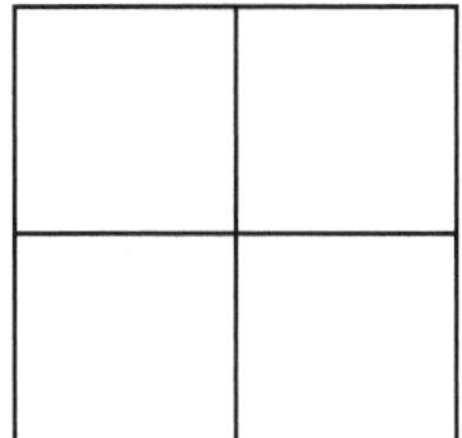
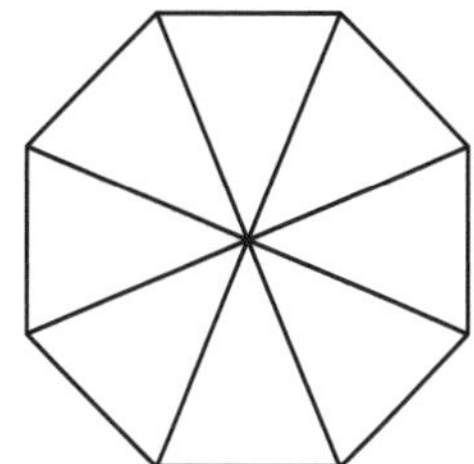
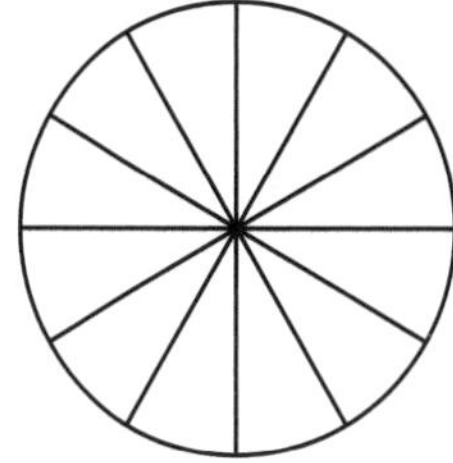

2. Circle all of the fractions below that are the same as $\frac{1}{5}$. 

$\frac{2}{10}$ $\frac{4}{16}$ $\frac{7}{12}$ $\frac{3}{15}$ $\frac{8}{20}$ $\frac{10}{50}$

3. Convert these fractions into percentages: 

$\frac{1}{4}$ = ... % $\frac{7}{10}$ = ... % $\frac{3}{6}$ = ... %

4. For each pair of fractions below, circle the biggest. 

$\frac{2}{7}$ or $\frac{3}{7}$ $\frac{1}{2}$ or $\frac{1}{3}$ $\frac{2}{3}$ or $\frac{5}{6}$

5. Write down the amount shown on the scales below.

a) 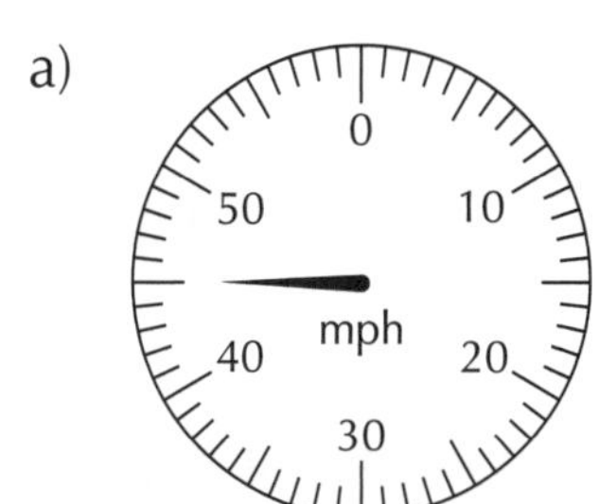

b) 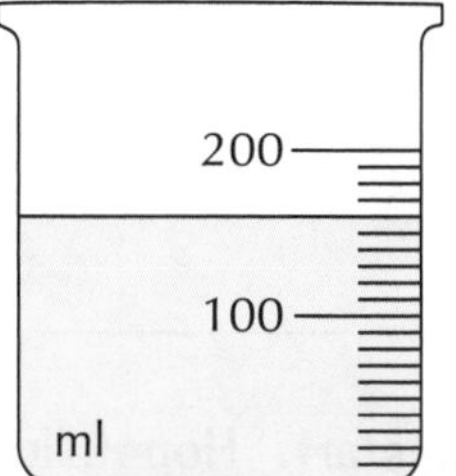

c) 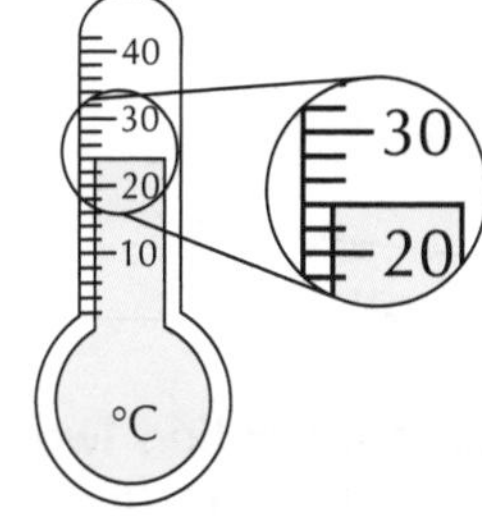

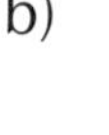
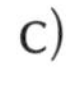

Don't forget to include the units.

....

Equivalent Fractions

1. Draw a line between each pair of equivalent fractions.

$\frac{1}{4}$ $\frac{4}{6}$ $\frac{3}{8}$ $\frac{5}{25}$

$\frac{6}{16}$ $\frac{1}{5}$ $\frac{3}{12}$ $\frac{2}{3}$

2. Debbie asks some of her classmates to name their favourite sport.

$\frac{2}{5}$ of them said speed knitting and $\frac{3}{8}$ said cricket.

a) Did more of her classmates say speed knitting or cricket?

....

b) Debbie asked 40 of her classmates in total. Six of them said that their favourite sport is football. What fraction of her classmates said football? Give your answer in its simplest form.

....

3. Julia, Parvinder and Richard are each given the same number of sweets. Julia eats $\frac{2}{5}$ of her sweets, Parvinder eats $\frac{5}{12}$ of his sweets and Richard eats $\frac{7}{15}$ of his sweets.

Write their names in order, starting with the person who has the fewest sweets left.

....

fewest sweets most sweets

How did you do?

Well, that got Section Two off to a flying start. Hopefully, you got a decent fraction of this stuff right. Once you're happy with it all, put a big tick in the boxes below. You should be able to:

- ☐ **Identify equivalent fractions.**
- ☐ **Compare the sizes of different fractions.**
- ☐ **Write fractions in their simplest form.**

Mixed Numbers and Improper Fractions

1. Show that $1\frac{2}{3}$ is bigger than $\frac{4}{3}$.

Convert one of the fractions so that they're both in the same form.

2. Convert between mixed numbers and improper fractions to complete this table.

Mixed Number	Improper Fraction
$3\frac{1}{2}$	....
....	$\frac{8}{5}$
....	$\frac{18}{7}$
$7\frac{2}{3}$	....

3. Write the following numbers in order, starting with the smallest.

$2\frac{3}{8}$ $\frac{3}{4}$ $3\frac{2}{7}$ $\frac{8}{3}$

.................., ..., ..., ...

4. Oliver's pet snail is $1\frac{2}{5}$ inches long and Jemma's pet grasshopper is $\frac{13}{9}$ inches long.

Whose pet is longer? Show your working.

....

How did you do?

Whole numbers and fractions together... Don't let this mixed number business get you all mixed up. Once you've got your head around it, tick off these boxes. By now, you should be able to:

☐ Convert between mixed numbers and improper fractions.

☐ Compare the sizes of mixed numbers and improper fractions.

Adding and Subtracting Fractions

1. Mary cuts a cake into six equal slices. She eats $\frac{1}{2}$ of it and her brother eats $\frac{1}{3}$ of it.

a) Shade the diagram to show how much of the cake has been eaten.

b) What fraction of the cake is left?

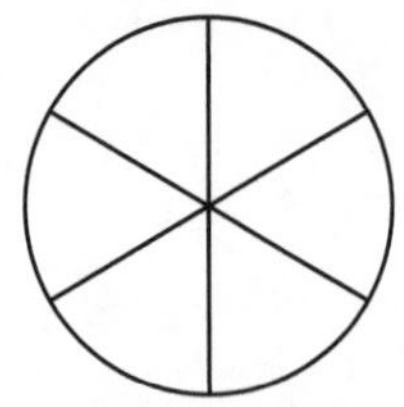

....

2. Work out the following, giving your answers as mixed numbers where necessary.

$\frac{1}{4} + \frac{2}{4}$ ....

$\frac{4}{3} - \frac{2}{3}$ ....

$1\frac{2}{7} + 2\frac{3}{7}$ ....

$3\frac{3}{7} - 1\frac{6}{7}$ ....

3. Frank wants to sell some apples at the market. $\frac{5}{19}$ of his apples have worms in and $\frac{3}{19}$ of the apples have gone rotten, so they can't be sold.

What fraction of his apples can Frank sell at the market?

....

4. A hiker sets off on a walk that is $10\frac{7}{8}$ miles long. She walks for $2\frac{3}{8}$ miles and then stops for lunch.

How many miles does she have left to walk?
Give your answer as a mixed number in its simplest form.

.... miles

Adding and Subtracting Fractions

5. A box of ice creams contains three different flavours. $\frac{1}{10}$ of the ice creams are chocolate flavour, $\frac{3}{5}$ are vanilla flavour and the rest are spinach flavour.

What fraction of the ice creams are spinach flavour?

....

6. Work out the following, giving your answers as mixed numbers (where necessary) in their simplest form.

$\frac{1}{2} + \frac{3}{4}$ ....

$\frac{15}{9} - 1\frac{5}{18}$ ....

$2\frac{4}{9} + 6\frac{2}{3}$ ....

7. Emily, Lei and Quentin picked some blackberries. They used identical baskets. Emily filled $1\frac{1}{2}$ baskets, Lei filled $\frac{7}{4}$ baskets and Quentin filled $1\frac{3}{8}$ baskets.

a) How many baskets of blackberries did they pick in total?
Write your answer as a mixed number in its simplest form.

....

b) A basket holds approximately 80 blackberries.
Estimate how many more blackberries Lei picked than Quentin.

....

How did you do?

This stuff is pretty key — you never know when you're going to need to add or subtract a fraction or two. Before you get too excited and move on to the next page, make sure you can:

☐ Add and subtract fractions with the same denominator.

☐ Use equivalent fractions to add and subtract fractions with different denominators.

Multiplying Fractions by Whole Numbers

1. Work out the following.

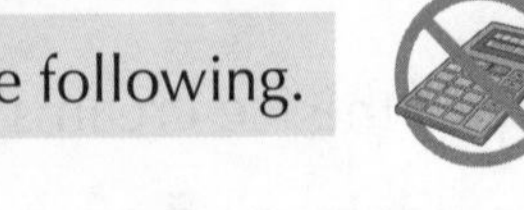

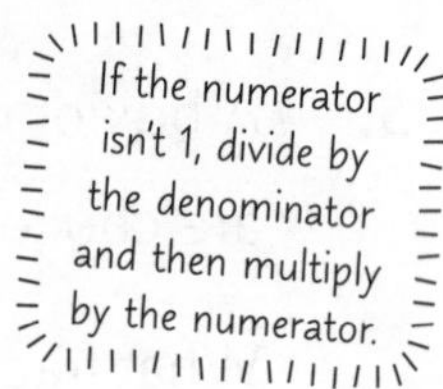

$\frac{1}{2} \times 32$ $\frac{1}{6} \times 48$ $\frac{3}{10} \times 100$

....

2. Amir has 120 marbles. $\frac{1}{10}$ of them are red and $\frac{2}{5}$ are green. The rest are purple.

a) How many of his marbles are red?

....

b) How many of his marbles are purple?

....

3. Work out the following. Give your answers as mixed numbers.

$\frac{1}{2} \times 15$ $\frac{2}{3} \times 11$ $\frac{3}{4} \times 22$

....

4. A robot works in a factory that makes red bananas. Each day, it makes 450 bananas.

The robot has a fault that means $\frac{2}{9}$ of the bananas it makes are blue.

a) How many blue bananas does the robot make each day?

....

The robot has some parts replaced. Now only $\frac{1}{15}$ of its bananas are blue.

b) How many fewer blue bananas does it make each day than before?

....

How did you do?

That's multiplying fractions by whole numbers covered — what fraction of this page did you get right? Give these a read and tick off each box once you're sure you can do it. You should be able to:

☐ **Multiply fractions by whole numbers.** ☐ **Find a fraction of an amount by multiplying.**

Fractions, Decimals and Percentages

1. Draw lines to match the values on the top row with an equivalent value on the bottom row.

0.24	35%	$\frac{9}{100}$	4.3	170%
430%	0.09	1.7	$\frac{12}{50}$	$\frac{7}{20}$

2. Convert...

a) 32% into a decimal,

....

b) $\frac{7}{25}$ into a percentage,

.... %

c) 0.54 into a fraction (in its simplest form).

....

3. Complete the table below by filling in the equivalent amounts.

Write any fractions in their simplest form.

Fraction	Decimal	Percentage
$\frac{9}{20}$	....	....
....	....	80%
....	0.24	....

4. Patrick looks at the sports kits of the teams in his hockey league. There are 20 teams in the league. 3 teams have stripy, orange kits.

a) What percentage of the teams have a stripy, orange hockey kit?

.... %

b) 40% of the teams have stripy kits.
What fraction of the teams have kits that are stripy but not orange?

....

Fractions, Decimals and Percentages

5. George scored 36 out of 40 in his maths test and 88% in his French test. Which subject did he score a higher proportion of the marks in?

....

6. Cathy has different vegetable plants growing in her greenhouse. $\frac{1}{4}$ of her plants are cucumbers, $\frac{3}{10}$ are tomatoes and $\frac{2}{5}$ are chillies.

   a) Cathy claims that 25% of her plants are chillies. Is she correct? Explain your reasoning.

   ....

   ....

   b) What percentage of her plants are not cucumbers, tomatoes or chillies?

   ....%

7. A film magazine publishes a list of the '25 Best Horror Films About Whales'.

   a) Joseph has watched 14 of the films on the list. Write the proportion of the films he has watched as a decimal.

   Find the proportion as a fraction first, then convert to a decimal.

   ....

   Over the weekend, Joseph watches another 24% of the films on the list.

   b) What fraction of the films on the list has he watched now? Give your answer in its simplest form.

   ....

How did you do?

With a bit of practice, you'll be switching between fractions, decimals and percentages like you've been doing it your whole life. Before you move on to the next bit, check that you can:

☐ **Switch between equivalent fractions, decimals and percentages.**

Finding Percentages Without a Calculator

1. Work out the following.

Remember that % means 'out of 100', so e.g. 35% means '35 out of 100'.

35% of 100 ....

10% of 170 ....

20% of 200 ....

2. Evan has a book of 80 knitting patterns. 30% of the patterns are for scarves and 10% of the patterns are for hats.

a) How many of the knitting patterns are for scarves?

....

b) How many of the knitting patterns are for neither scarves nor hats?

....

3. Tanya collects football stickers. She opens a box of 150 stickers and keeps only the stickers that she doesn't already own.

a) She already owns a copy of 12% of the stickers in the box.
How many of the stickers in the box does she keep?

....

b) 60% of the stickers in the box are of players from Rollerham Rovers, her favourite team.
If she already owns seven of these, how many of them does she keep?

....

How did you do?

You made it — and all without your calculator, no less. The good news is that you can get your calculator back out soon. Tick off the boxes below when you're 100% sure that you:

- [ ] Understand that 'percentage' means 'out of 100'.
- [ ] Can find percentages without using a calculator.

Finding Percentages Using a Calculator

1. Work out the following.

You can either multiply by the equivalent decimal or use your calculator's % button.

18% of 250 ....

4% of 675 ....

162% of 1050 ....

2. Lukas is given £26 for his birthday. He spends 11% of the money on a magazine about kangaroos and donates a further 57% of the money to a koala hospital.

a) How much money did Lukas donate to the hospital?

£ ....

b) How much money does Lukas have left?

£ ....

3. A greengrocer has an offer where customers get 23% extra free on their shopping.

a) Pauline buys 860 g of plums.
How many grams of plums does Pauline receive for free?

23% EXTRA FREE

.... g

12% discount
OR
£4 off your bill

The sign on the left shows two offers available from a butcher.

b) Pauline's bill comes to £37 before either offer is applied.
Which offer will save her the most money? Tick your answer.

☐ 12% discount ☐ £4 off your bill

How did you do?

Calculators are allowed on this page and that's always a pleasure. By now, you should be able to:

☐ **Find percentages using a calculator.**

Ratios and Comparing

1. Look at the image on the right.
What is the ratio of sea lions to balls?

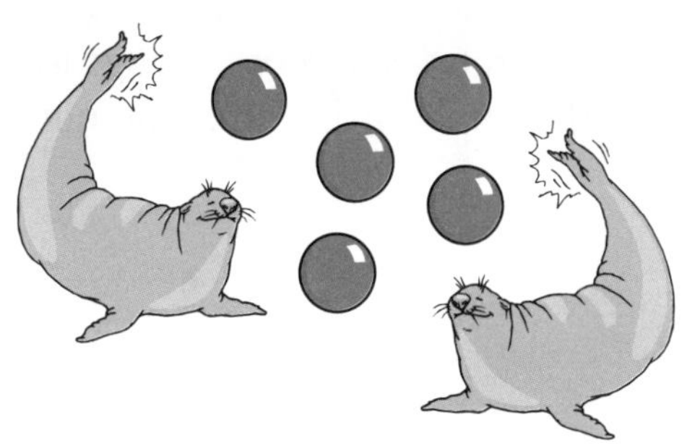

.... : ....

2. In this question, write any fractions in their simplest form.

Write 15 as a fraction of 25.

....

Write 60 as a fraction of 42.

....

Write 12 as a percentage of 48.

.... %

Write 30 as a percentage of 20.

.... %

3. Look at the picture of pizza slices and carrots.

a) Tick the box that's next to the correct ratio of pizza slices to carrots.

☐ 3 : 6 ☐ 6 : 2 ☐ 6 : 3 ☐ 6 : 9

b) What is the ratio of pizza slices to carrots in its simplest form?

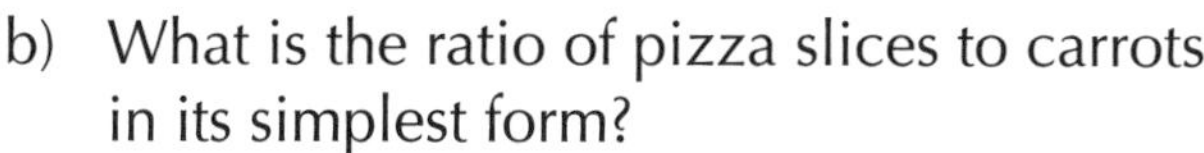

.... : ....

4. Choose the correct tile from the cloud to make each of these statements true.

10% of 70 ☐ 20% of 25

$\frac{3}{4}$ of 40 ☐ $\frac{3}{2}$ of 20

$\frac{2}{3}$ of 21 ☐ $\frac{3}{8}$ of 32

15% of 60 ☐ 25% of 40

Ratios and Comparing

5. The ratio of plates to mugs in a cupboard is 5 : 3. There are 10 plates in the cupboard. Circle the number of mugs that there are in the cupboard.

5 3 6 10 8

6. Deepak buys 2.6 m² of fabric and uses 1.95 m² of it to make a skirt.

a) Find the amount of fabric he uses as a fraction of the amount of fabric he bought. Give your answer in its simplest form.

....

b) He uses 0.52 m² of the leftover fabric to make a matching headband. What percentage of the leftover fabric does he use?

.... %

7. Orange juice comes in bottles of different sizes. William buys a 600 ml bottle and Irina buys a 1 litre bottle.

a) William drinks 240 ml of his bottle. What fraction of the bottle has he drunk? Give your answer in its simplest form.

....

b) Irina drinks 330 ml of her bottle. Who has drunk a larger percentage of their bottle? Show your working.

1 litre = 1000 ml

....

How did you do?

Another topic, over far too soon... Once you're confident you know what you're on about, enjoy the satisfying feeling of ticking off these boxes. You've earned it. By this point, you should be able to:

- ☐ Write one number as a fraction or a percentage of another number.
- ☐ Compare different amounts using fractions, percentages and ratios.
- ☐ Write ratios using the proper notation.
- ☐ Reduce ratios to their simplest form.

Time

1. Aleks goes to bed at 10:10 pm and Alexis goes to bed at 22:22.

Who goes to bed at the later time?

....

2. The clocks below show times in the afternoon or evening. Write down the time on each one using the 12-hour clock and the 24-hour clock.

12-hour: .... 12-hour: .... 12-hour: ....

24-hour: .... 24-hour: .... 24-hour: ....

3. Zara can either walk or cycle between home and school. The journey takes 48 minutes to walk or 22 minutes to cycle.

a) Zara leaves school at 15:49 and cycles home. What time will she arrive? Give your answer in the 24-hour clock.

....

b) What time would Zara need to leave home to walk to school and arrive at 08:30? Give your answer in the 12-hour clock.

....

4. Convert...

a) 180 minutes into hours,

.... hours

b) 2.5 hours into minutes,

.... minutes

c) $5\frac{1}{4}$ minutes into seconds.

.... seconds

Time

5. Below is part of a bus timetable.

Neptune Street	06:54	07:18	07:33	07:48
Drumlin Lane	07:08	07:32	07:47	08:02
Redmile Road	07:17	07:41	07:56	08:11
Mortimer Crescent	07:32	07:56	08:11	08:26

a) Janet needs to arrive at Redmile Road by 08:00. What is the latest time she can catch a bus from Neptune Street and arrive at Redmile Road without being late?

....

b) How long does it take to get from Drumlin Lane to Mortimer Crescent?

.... minutes

c) Olga wants to catch the 07:56 bus from Mortimer Crescent, but it doesn't leave Redmile Road until 07:52. What time can she expect the bus to arrive?

....

6. The schedule for a family fun day is shown on the right.

a) What time does Afternoon Tea start in the 12-hour clock?

....

b) How many minutes later does Sandcastle Building start than Sock Puppet Shakespeare?

.... minutes

c) Sandcastle Building lasts for 85 minutes and the Medieval Costume Contest starts immediately after. Fill in the start time of the Medieval Costume Contest on the schedule, writing it in the 24-hour clock.

Time	Event
13:00	Harmonica Recital
14:10	Balloon Animal Workshop
15:25	Afternoon Tea
16:15	Sock Puppet Shakespeare
17:55	Sandcastle Building
....	Medieval Costume Contest

How did you do?

Once you've got this stuff covered, you'll never miss the bus again. Time to make sure you can:

- ☐ **Convert between 12- and 24-hour clocks.**
- ☐ **Convert between different units of time (seconds, minutes and hours).**
- ☐ **Solve problems that involve time, e.g. interpreting and using timetables.**

Units and Measuring

1. Use the ruler below to complete this question.

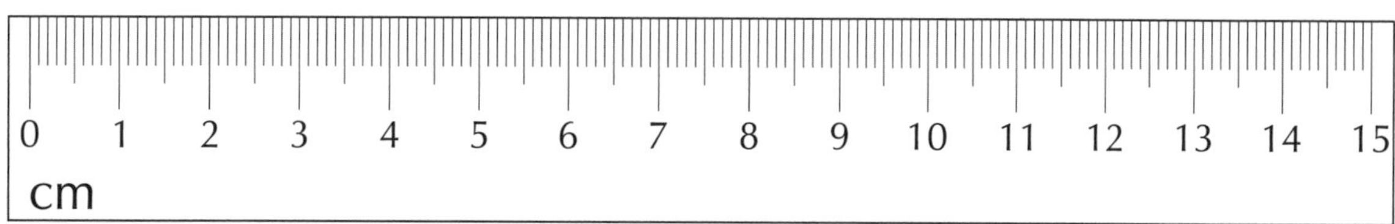

a) Draw an arrow pointing to the mark representing 13.5 cm and label it A.

b) Draw an arrow pointing to the mark representing 37 mm and label it B.

c) Draw an arrow pointing to the mark representing 0.07 m and label it C.

2. Circle the amounts below that are equal to 550 cm. 

0.55 km　　5.5 m　　55 000 mm　　5500 mm

3. Write these measurements in order of size, starting with the smallest. 

2.3 cm	24 mm	0.2 m	21 cm	2.3 mm

....

4. Convert: 

4.23 litres into ml

.... ml

76 g into kg

.... kg

5. Convert 287 mm into metres. 

Convert into centimetres first, then from centimetres into metres.

.... m

Units and Measuring

6. Wanda has completed a triathlon. She swam for 750 m, cycled for 19.4 km and ran for 5000 m. What was the total distance, in kilometres, of the triathlon?

.... km

7. Kirsten uses the ingredients on the right to make a batch of shortbread.

Shortbread	
525 g	flour
175 g	sugar
0.35 kg	butter

a) What is the total mass of the ingredients in kilograms?

.... kg

b) One shortbread biscuit uses a total of 30 g of the ingredients. Kirsten needs at least 32 biscuits to give out to her class. Will this recipe make enough?

....

8. Owen makes some fruit punch. He uses 750 ml of cranberry juice, 0.45 litres of pineapple juice, 320 ml of orange juice and 1.3 litres of lemonade.

a) How many litres of fruit punch does Owen make?

.... litres

b) Owen pours the punch into glasses that can each hold 180 ml of liquid. How many whole glasses can he fill?

....

c) How much punch is left over after he has filled as many glasses as possible? Give your answer in millilitres.

.... ml

How did you do?

The last topic of Section Two, all finished... How exciting. I'm sure you know the drill by now — once you're confident you understand all this stuff, tick off these boxes. You should be able to:

☐ Use different units of measurement.

☐ Read values from different scales.

☐ Convert between standard units of measurement for mass, length and capacity.

Section Two — Review Exercise

There's just the Review Exercise to go, and then you're all done with Section Two. It's a bit sad, really. Take a crack at these to see how much you've picked up.

1. Write the following fractions in their simplest forms. 

a) $\frac{6}{18}$ b) $\frac{8}{28}$ c) $\frac{45}{36}$

.... 

3 marks

2. Put the following in order from smallest to largest. 

$\frac{9}{4}$ $\frac{7}{12}$ $1\frac{2}{3}$ $\frac{11}{5}$ $2\frac{1}{9}$

.........., ..., ..., ..., ...

2 marks

3. Work out the following calculations.
Give your answers as mixed numbers where necessary. 

a) $\frac{5}{9} + \frac{1}{3}$ b) $2\frac{3}{10} - \frac{2}{5}$

.... 

2 marks

4. Lewis has 60 songs on a playlist. $\frac{2}{5}$ of them are rock songs and $\frac{7}{20}$ are jazz. 

a) What percentage of the songs on the playlist are jazz songs?

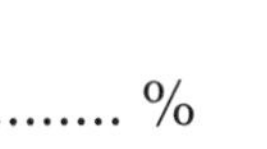
.... %

1 mark

b) How many of the songs are rock songs?

....

1 mark

c) How many songs are neither rock nor jazz?

....

2 marks

Section Two — Review Exercise

5. An animal adoption centre has 40 cats. 30% of them are ginger. How many of the cats are ginger?

.... 1 mark

6. Work out the following.

a) 15 as a fraction of 45

You should give the fraction in its simplest form.

....

b) 21 as a percentage of 7

.... %

2 marks

7. Look at the picture on the right. Write down the ratio of needles to haystacks.

.... : ....

1 mark

8. A train travelling to London departs from Manchester at 11:47. It arrives in London at 14:09, 14 minutes later than scheduled. How long would the journey have taken if the train had arrived on time? Give your answer in hours and minutes.

.... hours .... minutes

2 marks

9. Yan is making jam for a bake sale. The amounts of jam she already has are shown on the right. She needs 1.2 kg in total. How much more jam, in grams, does she need?

Yan's Jams	
0.125 kg	cherry jam
0.45 kg	grape jam
385 g	apricot jam

.... g

2 marks

Bonus question — find out what percentage of these you got right...

And that's a wrap on Section Two. It's a common misconception that percentages have to be less than 100 or that fractions have to be less than 1. That said, 19/19 is the highest score you can get in this exercise — so you're not getting more than 100% here, no matter how neat your handwriting is.

Score: ____ / **19**

Section Three — Algebra and Graphs

This section is all about algebra... Using letters instead of numbers may seem a bit weird but they're only there to represent numbers you don't know yet. See what you know already with these starter questions.

Before you Start

1. A sequence begins 26, 34, 42, 50, ☐, 66...
   Circle the number below that fills the gap in the sequence.

   54 60 63 58 52

2. Write the next three terms and the term-to-term rule of each sequence.
   The first one has been done for you.

   a) –9, –6, –3, 0, ..3..., ..6..., ..9... ....Add 3........

   b) 5, 10, 15, 20, ..., ..., ...

   c) 31, 27, 23, 19, ..., ..., ...

3. The perimeter of a rectangle has the formula $P = l + w + l + w$.
   Find P when $l = 5$ cm and $w = 2$ cm.

   $P =$ ....

4. Write a pair of positive whole numbers, x and y, that fit the equation $x + 2y = 5$.

   $x =$ .... $y =$ ....

5. Look at the coordinate grid below.

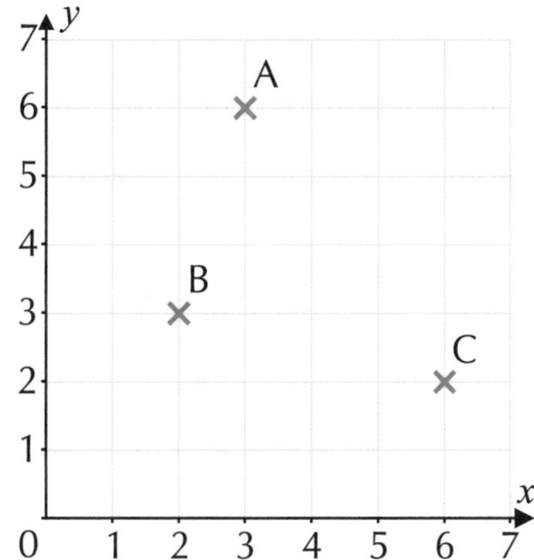

   a) Write down the coordinates of the points A, B and C.

   A = ... B = ... C = ...

   b) Plot the point with coordinates (4, 5) on the grid and label it D.

Simplifying Expressions

1. Collect all of the terms in the bubbles to write a simplified expression.

It might help if you cross off the terms as you go to help you keep track.

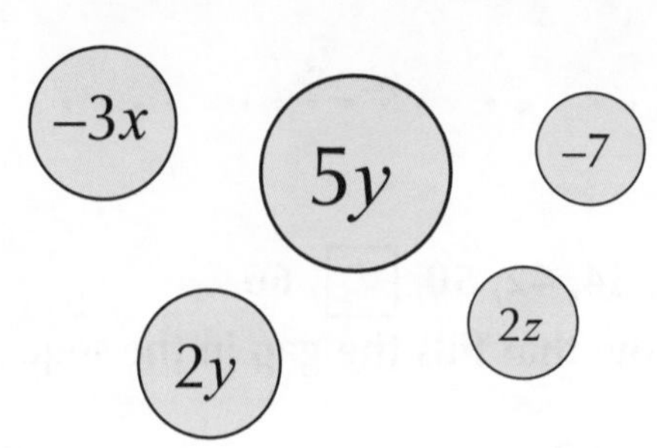
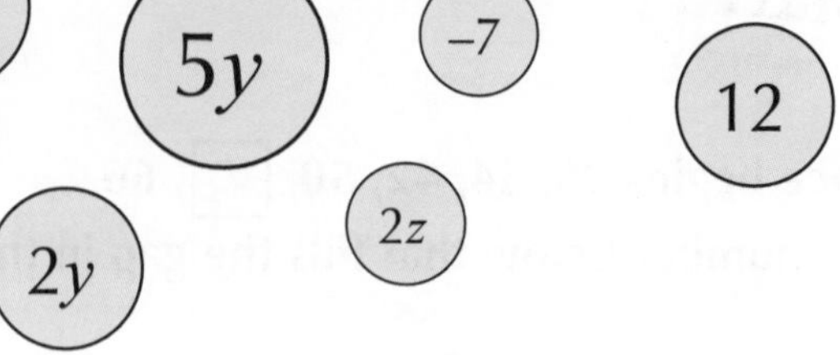

....

2. Simplify the following expressions, then circle the odd one out.

a) $2x + 2y - y$

b) $6y + 5y - 2x + 7 - 4y$

c) $6x + y + 5 - 3 - 4x - 2$

....

3. Draw a line joining each expression with its simplified form.

$3a + a + b$	$a \times 2a \times b$	$2a \div 4b$	$6b - a + a$	$a \times b \div 3a$
$\frac{a}{2b}$	$4a + b$	$6b$	$\frac{b}{3}$	$2a^2b$

4. At full price, jackets cost £x and shirts cost £y. During a sale, each jacket has £15 off and shirts are sold at half-price.

a) Which of these is an expression for the cost of a jacket and 4 shirts during a sale? Circle your answer.

$\frac{1}{2}(x + 4y) - 15$ $\quad (x - 15) + (4 \times \frac{1}{2}y)$ $\quad \frac{1}{2}(x + 4y - 15)$

b) Write this expression in its simplified form.

....

How did you do?

Cor blimey, that's the first topic of Section Three finished already. The section might be new, but some things just never change — tick off these boxes when you're confident that you can:

☐ Use algebraic notation correctly.

☐ Collect like terms to simplify expressions.

Solving Equations

1. Find the value of each letter.

a) $a + 10 = 60$ $a =$ ....

b) $19 + b = 31$ $b =$ ....

c) $c - 16 = 20$ $c =$ ....

d) $d + 8 = 4$ $d =$ ....

2. Ellis needs help solving the equations below.
Draw lines to join each unknown with its value.

$4a = 12$ $5b = 25$ $\frac{c}{2} = 4$ $\frac{d}{3} = 3$

(a)	(8)
(b)	(9)
(c)	(3)
(d)	(5)

3. Solve the following equations.

a) $2a + 3 = 13$ b) $8b - 3 = 21$ c) $10c + 12 = 72$ d) $50d - 100 = 250$

$a =$ .... $b =$ .... $c =$ .... $d =$ ....

4. Samira solves an equation to get $x = 3$.

Circle all the equations below that she could have solved.

$3x + 2 = 11$ $7x = 21$ $89 - x = 92$

$18x = 36$ $3x - 2 = 2$ $5x + 3 = 18$

5. Answer true (☑) or false (☒) to show whether the equations have the solution $x = 2$.

a) $7x = 12$ ☐ b) $3x - 3 = 3$ ☐ c) $5 - x = 4$ ☐ d) $8x + 9 = 25$ ☐

Solving Equations

6. Greg and Hannah shared a bag of popcorn whilst watching 'The Equatables' at the cinema. The bag contained 62 pieces of popcorn. Hannah ate n pieces, Greg ate $4n$ pieces and there were 7 pieces left over.

a) Circle the equation that could be used to find n.

$n + 4 + 7 = 62$ $5n - 7 = 62$ $4n + 7 = 62$ $5n + 7 = 62$

b) How many pieces of popcorn did Hannah eat?

....

7. Draw a line to match each equation on the left to the equation on the right that, when solved, gives the same value for x.

$3x - 2 = 4$	$3x - 5 = -2x$
$4x = 4$	$2x - 5 = 1$
$4x - 3 = 9$	$7x - 10 = 2x$

8. Look at the equation in the box: $17x = 510$

Use it to write down the answers to the following, without solving the equation:

a) $17x + 31 =$ ....   b) $170x =$ ....   c) $1700x - 500 =$ ....

9. If $4x - 9 = 2x + 3$, find x.

$x =$ ....

How did you do?

Phew, that was a bit of a workout. Don't let the more complicated equations get you in a muddle — just go slowly and tackle it one step at a time. Take a second to make sure that you know how to:

☐ Solve equations with one unknown value.

☐ Rearrange equations into a form you can solve.

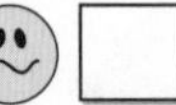

Substituting into Expressions and Formulas

1. Find the value of the following expressions.

a) $5b - 3$ when $b = 6$

b) $10p + 7w$ when $p = 2$ and $w = 4$

c) $100 + 3d - 8j$ when $d = 5$ and $j = 3$

2. Write the expressions in order from smallest to largest when $t = 4$.

$3t + 7$ $33 - 6t$ $\frac{10t}{2}$ $50t - 189$

....

3. The formula linking speed (s), distance (d) and time (t) is:

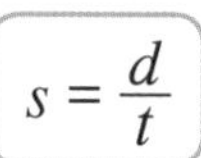

$s = \frac{d}{t}$

Find s when $d = 27$ and $t = 3$.

$s =$ ....

4. The formula on the right gives the number of minutes, T, it takes to bake a potato that weighs w kg.

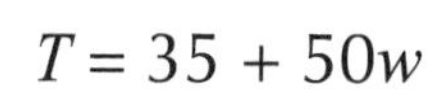

$T = 35 + 50w$

a) Ed's potato weighs 0.5 kg. How many minutes should he bake it for?

.... minutes

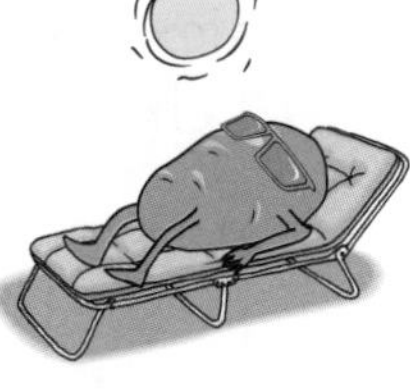

b) Nish only has 50 minutes to bake a potato.
What is the mass of the heaviest potato that can be baked in this time?

.... kg

How did you do?

And that's another topic in the bag... Tick off the boxes once you're happy that you can:

☐ Substitute numbers into expressions.

☐ Substitute numbers into formulas.

Sequences

1. For each of these sequences, draw a line to match the sequence to the term-to-term rule.

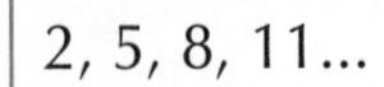

2, 5, 8, 11...	Divide by 2
67, 56, 45, 34....	Add 4
3, 6 ,12, 24...	Add 3
–3, 1, 5, 9...	Subtract 11
16, 8, 4, 2...	Multiply by 2
2, –5, –12, –19...	Subtract 7

2. Fill in the missing terms of the following sequences.

a) –3, 6, ..., 24, 33

b) ...., 12, 17, ..., 27

c) –2, ..., –18, –26, ...

d) 28, ..., ..., 16, 12

3. The numbers of this sequence have been scrambled up. Put them back into order and write down the term-to-term rule. The first number has been done for you.

39	31	23	35	27

39, ..., ..., ..., ...

Rule: ....

4. Alex has a box of 40 chocolates. Each day, she eats 3 chocolates and gives her sister 2 chocolates.

a) Write down the first five terms of the sequence formed by the number of chocolates she has left at the end of each day.

.........., ..., ..., ..., ...

b) She was given the chocolates and starts eating them on her birthday. Counting her birthday as day 1, at the end of which day will the box be empty?

Day ....

Sequences

5. A squirrel arranges acorns into piles that form the following sequence.

1 2 3

a) Complete the following table.

Pattern Number	1	2	3	4	5
Number of Acorns	....	....	....	....	....

b) How many acorns will be in the 10th pattern?

....

6. Maj is bored in class and makes some patterns out of pencils.

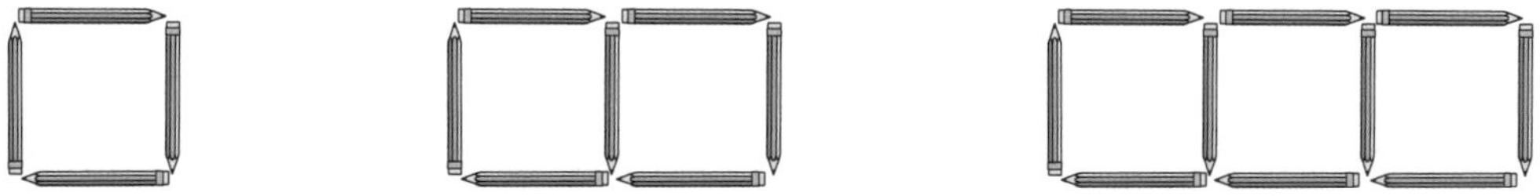

Pattern 1 Pattern 2 Pattern 3

a) Draw the next pattern in the sequence.

b) How many pencils does he use to make Pattern 7?

.... pencils

How did you do?

Sequences are all about spotting patterns... And you might have spotted the pattern in what I'm about to ask you to do next. That's right — tick off the boxes when you're happy that you can:

☐ Identify the rule to get from one term in a sequence to the next.

☐ Find missing terms in a sequence of numbers or shapes.

Coordinates

1. A pirate can't remember the code to his treasure chest, but his parrot says the letters are on the map at coordinates (7, 8), (2, 2), (11, 1), (5, 6) and (5, 10). Write down the letters of the code that will open his treasure chest.

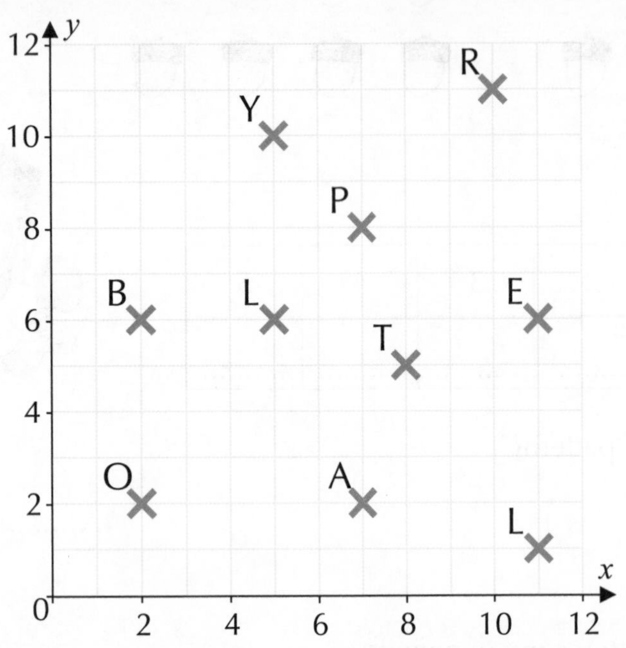

.........., ..., ..., ..., ...

2. Dembe plotted some points on the grid below, but forgot to label them with their coordinates. Draw lines between the boxes to match the letters to the coordinates.

A	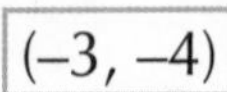 (–3, –4)
B	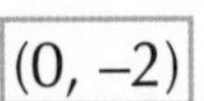 (0, –2)
C	(4, –3)
D	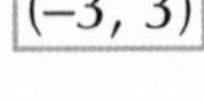 (–3, 3)
E	(–2, 0)
F	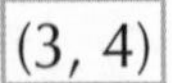 (3, 4)

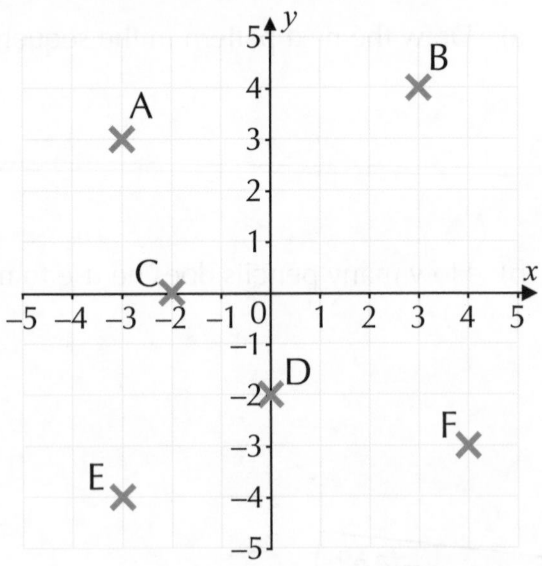

3. Circle the coordinates below where the x-coordinate is double the y-coordinate.

(3, 6)   (10, 5)   (2, 0)   (4, 2)   (3, 5)

Coordinates

4. Which of these pairs of coordinates lie on a vertical line? Tick all the correct answers.

☐ (1, 2) & (1, 3)   ☐ (2, 4) & (1, 4)   ☐ (–6, 2) & (–6, 1)   ☐ (–3, –3) & (–3, 3)

5. Look at the coordinate grid on the right.

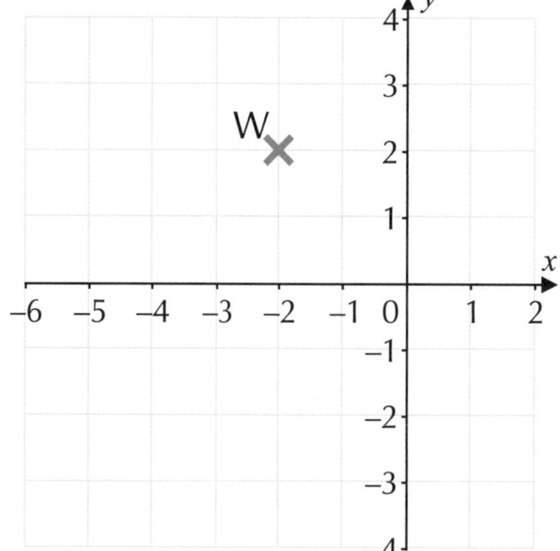

a) Write down the coordinates of point W.

....

b) Plot and label the points X (–5, –1) and Y (–2, –4) on the grid.

c) W, X and Y are three vertices of a square. Write down the coordinates of the fourth vertex.

....

6. Look at the coordinate grid below.

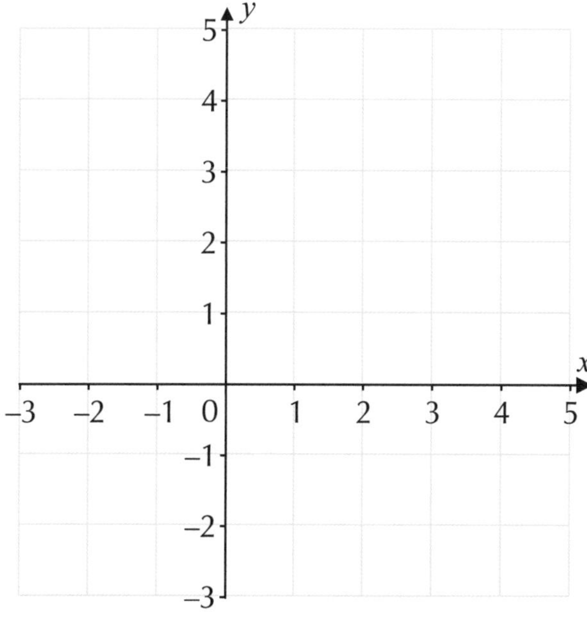

a) Plot and label the points A (4, 2), B (–1, 1) and C (4, –1) on the grid.

b) (i) Draw the lines AC and BC.

(ii) The point D is the fourth vertex of a parallelogram ADBC. What are the coordinates of D?

....

How did you do?

When it comes to finding coordinates, always remember to go across first, and then up or down. Tick off these boxes before you move on to the next page. By now, you should be able to:

☐ Read coordinates off of a grid with four quadrants.

☐ Plot coordinates on a grid with four quadrants.

 ☐  ☐ ☐

Section Three — Review Exercise

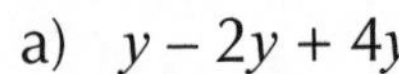

1. Simplify the following expressions.

a) $y - 2y + 4y$

....

b) $x \times x \times 3y$

....

2 marks

2. Solve these equations.

a) $7x = 14$

$x =$ ....

b) $9 + x = 81$

$x =$ ....

c) $7x + 8 = 43$

$x =$ ....

d) $25x - 7 = 143$

$x =$ ....

4 marks

3. Solve the equations below.

a) $3x - 7 = 17$

$x =$ ....

b) $7x = 44 - 4x$

$x =$ ....

4 marks

4. Find the value of the following expressions. 

a) $7b + 8$ when $b = 4$

....

1 mark

b) $3 - 4s$ when $s = 3$

....

1 mark

c) $-7 - 8m + 2n$ when $m = 2$ and $n = 3$

....

2 marks

5. The formula on the right is for the cost, C (in £), of hiring roller skates for h hours.
What is the cost of hiring roller skates for 4 hours?

$$C = 2h + 15$$

£ ....

1 mark

Section Three — Review Exercise

6. A sequence begins –8, –2, S, 10, 16...

a) What is the value of the missing term S? Explain how you found your answer.

....

2 marks

b) Does the sequence above contain any numbers that are in the sequence beginning –7, –1, 5, 11, 17...? Explain your answer.

....

2 marks

7. Jane makes the following sequence out of doughnuts.

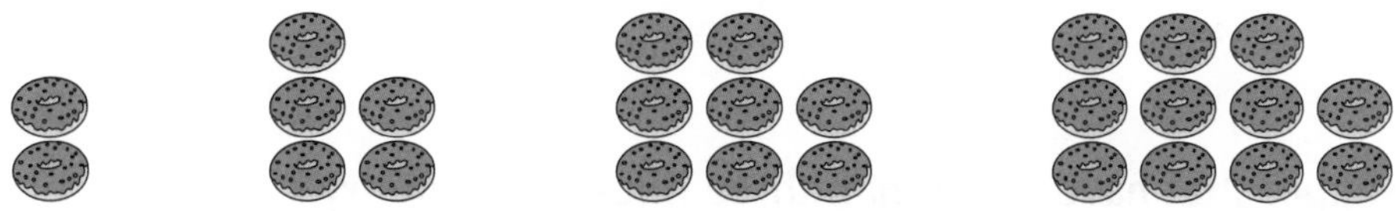

a) Draw the next two patterns in the sequence.

2 marks

b) How many doughnuts are in the 7th pattern?

....

1 mark

8. Look at the coordinate grid on the right.

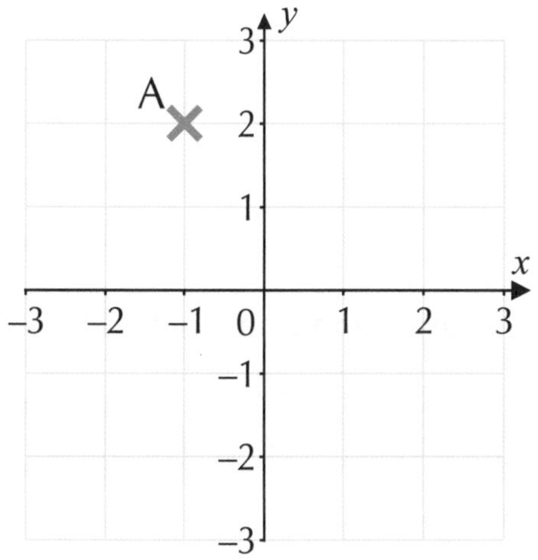

a) Write down the coordinates of the point A.

....

1 mark

b) Plot and label the points B (3, 1), C (2, –1) and D (–3, –2) on the grid.

2 marks

c) What shape is formed by A, B, C and D?

....

1 mark

If only you could simplify every maths question...

Some people think algebra is scary, but hopefully this section showed you it's not all that bad. When you're faced with an equation to solve, remember that the 'x' is just a number you don't know yet — it follows all the same old maths rules you've been using for years, so there's no need to panic.

Score: ____ / **26**

Section Four — Geometry

Welcome to a whole section on geometry. You'll find all the shapes, angles and lines you could ever want. I know — you can thank me later. First up, let's see how much you know with the questions below.

Before you Start

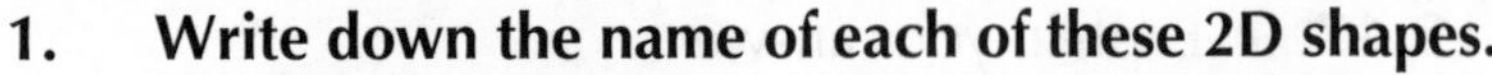

1. Write down the name of each of these 2D shapes.

a) 

b)  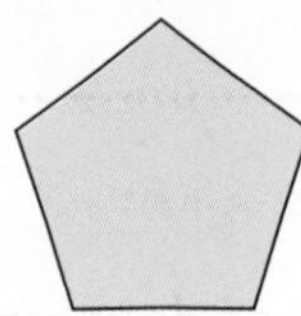

c) 

....

2. Circle the shapes that have more than three lines of symmetry.

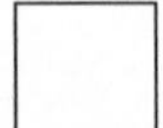 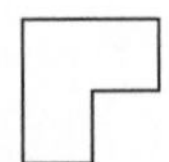 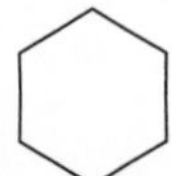 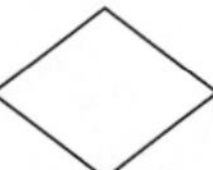 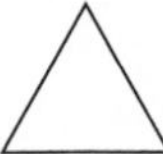 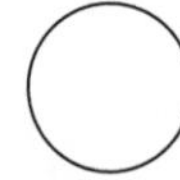

3. Use a ruler to measure the straight line below. Write your answer on the dotted line.

.... cm

4. Write down whether each of these angles is acute, obtuse or reflex.

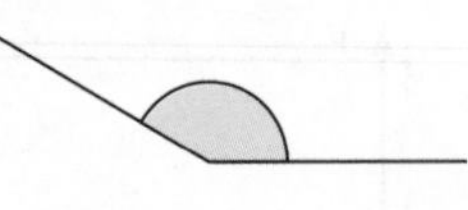 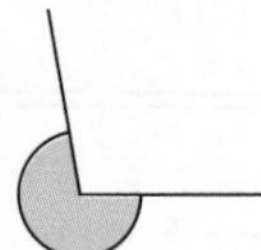 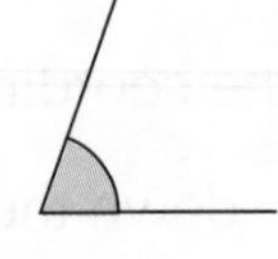

....

5. Draw a line from each of these 3D shapes to its name.

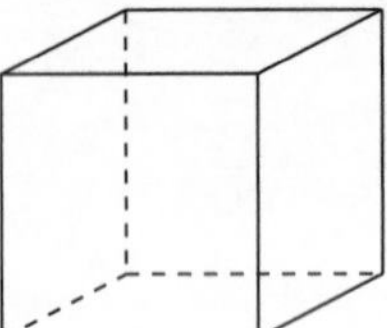 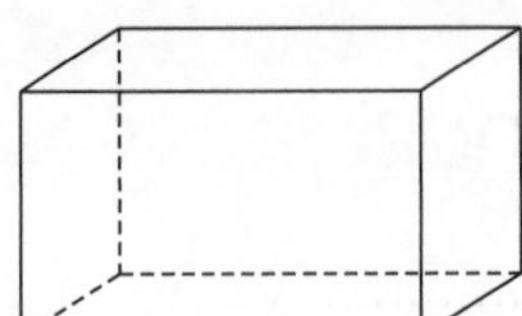 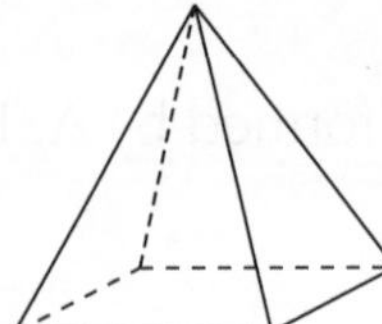 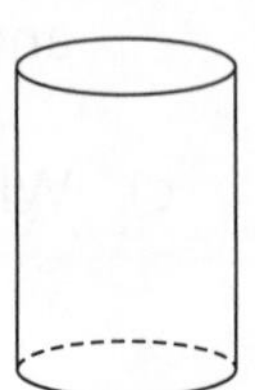

Pyramid	Triangular Prism	Cube	Cylinder	Sphere	Cuboid

Symmetry

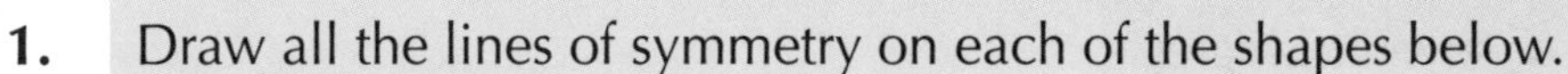

1. Draw all the lines of symmetry on each of the shapes below.

a) 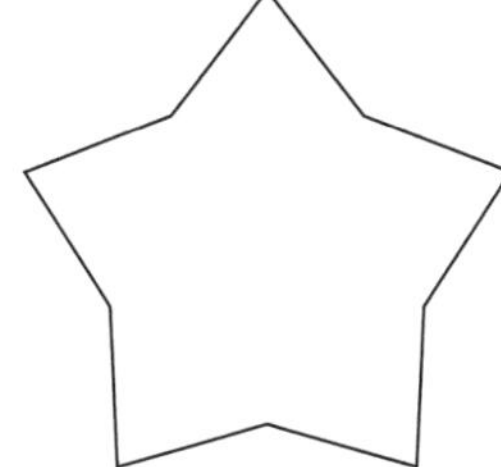

b) 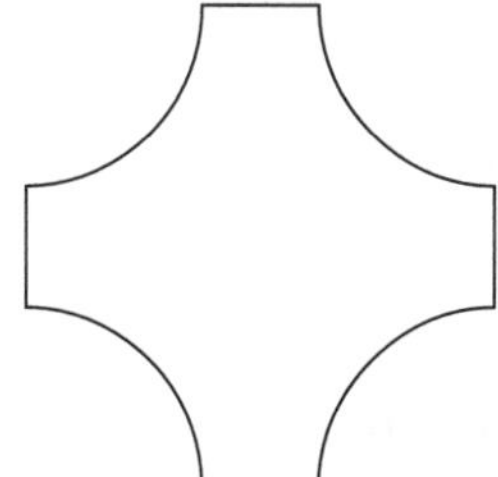

c) 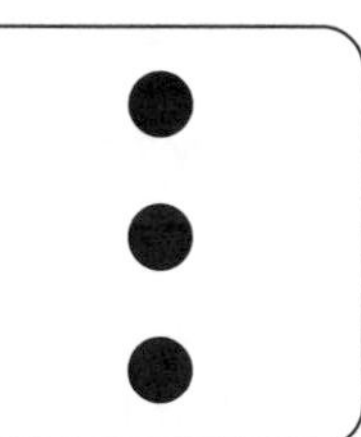

2. Draw lines to match each shape with its order of rotational symmetry.

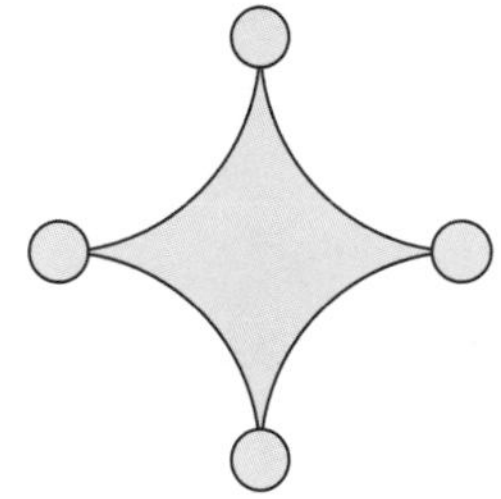

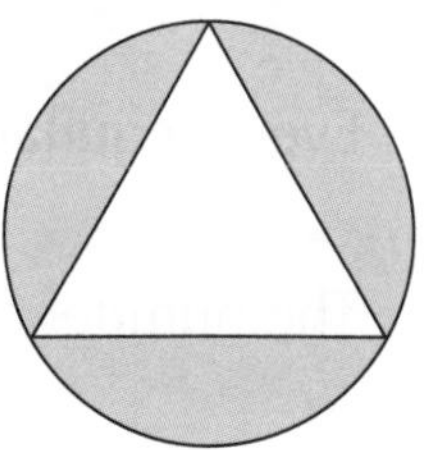

Two

Three

Four

3. Shade four squares in the pattern below so that is has exactly one vertical line of symmetry.

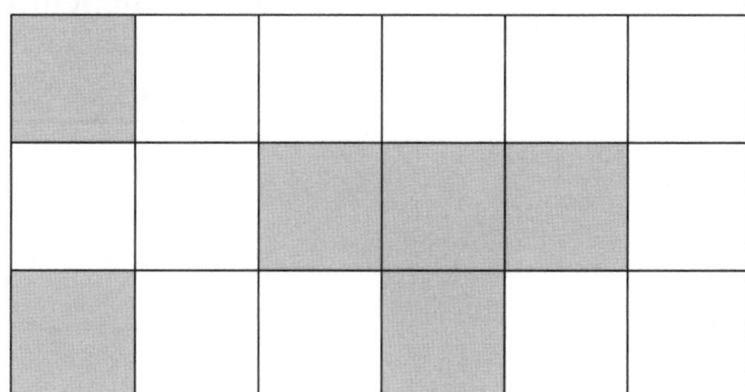

How did you do?

First page of the section — done! Good job. Now you should be able to:

☐ Find and draw lines of symmetry on shapes.

☐ Find the order of rotational symmetry of shapes.

Properties of Triangles

1. Ms. Anne Gular is made up of seven triangles.

a) Shade all of the isosceles triangles.

b) How many right-angled triangles are there?

....

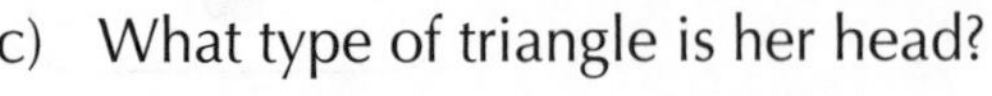

c) What type of triangle is her head?

....

2. Complete these sentences by underling the correct words.

a) Every (**equilateral** / **isosceles**) triangle has three equal angles.

b) The number of equal angles in a scalene triangle is (**zero** / **two**).

c) A right-angled triangle (**always** / **sometimes** / **never**) has one line of symmetry.

d) It's (**possible** / **impossible**) to draw a triangle with rotational symmetry of order 2.

3. Two points have been drawn on each of these grids.

Draw a third point on the bold line and then join them up to create:

a) an isosceles triangle

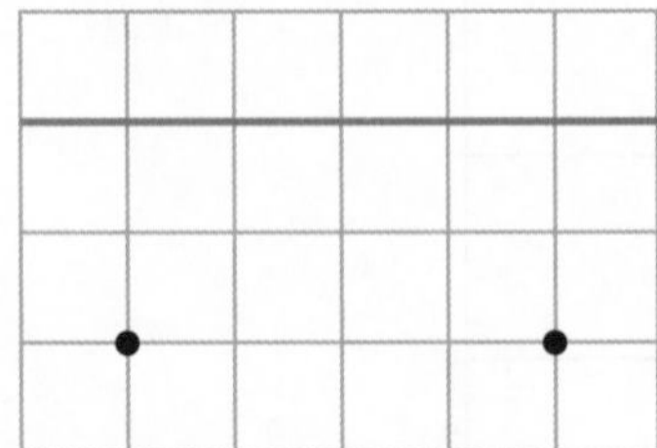

b) a scalene triangle

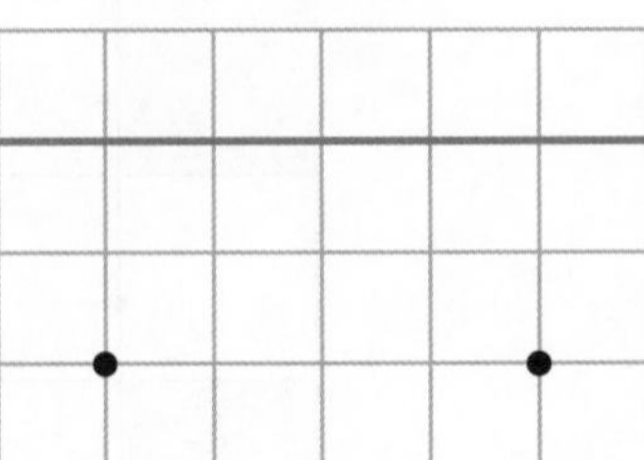

How did you do?

Triangles can be pointy creatures at first — but get to know them and you'll learn to love them. Once you're good pals, you should:

☐ Be able to name and identify the different types of triangles.

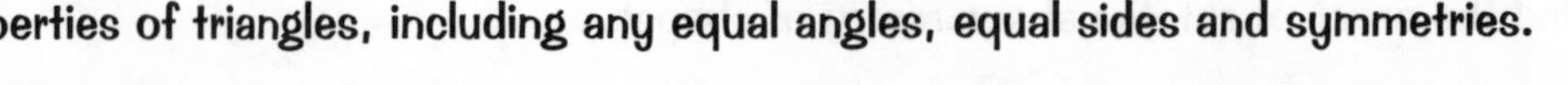

☐ Know the properties of triangles, including any equal angles, equal sides and symmetries.

Properties of Quadrilaterals

1. Name all the quadrilaterals that have the following properties.

Your answers should come from the list on the right.

a) Two pairs of parallel sides

....

b) Diagonals that cross at 90°

....

c) The possibility to have **exactly** one obtuse angle

....

Square
Rectangle
Rhombus
Parallelogram
Kite
Trapezium

2. Tick all the statements that are true for a rhombus.

☐ It has four sides of equal length.

☐ It has two lines of symmetry.

☐ All four sides are different lengths.

☐ It has four equal angles.

☐ It has two pairs of equal angles.

☐ It has no lines of symmetry.

3. Two sides of a quadrilateral have been drawn on each of these grids.

Draw a fourth point and then join them up to create:

a) a kite

b) a trapezium

How did you do?

Quadrilaterals are 2D shapes with four sides. Each type of quadrilateral comes with its own set of properties, so you just have to learn them all. After working through this page you should:

☐ Be able to name and identify the different types of quadrilaterals.

☐ Know the properties of quadrilaterals, i.e. any equal angles or sides, parallel sides and symmetries.

Angle Rules

None of the diagrams on this page are drawn accurately.

1. Find the missing angles.

a) 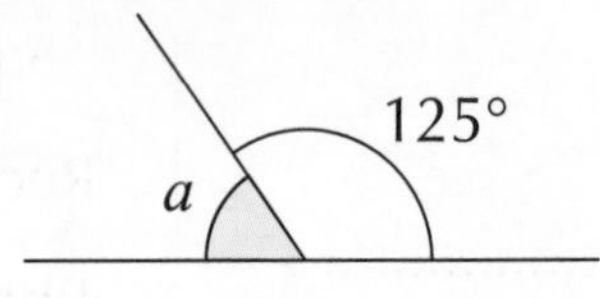

$a =$ .... °

b) 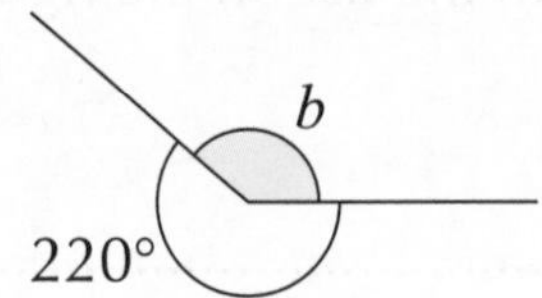

$b =$ .... °

c) 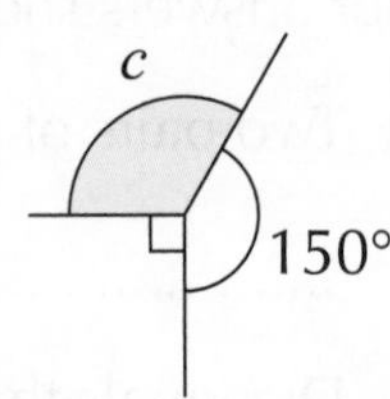

$c =$ .... °

2. Find the missing angles.

a) 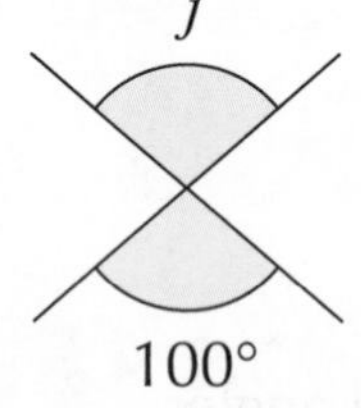

$j =$ .... °

b) 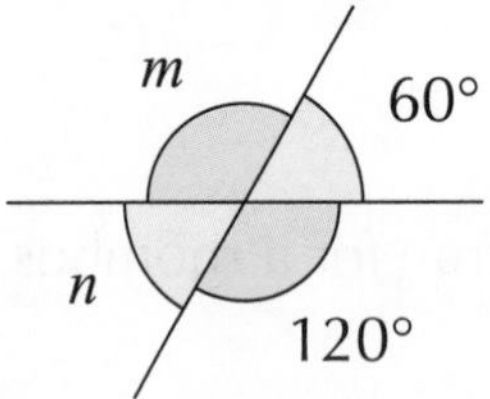

$m =$ .... °

$n =$ .... °

c) 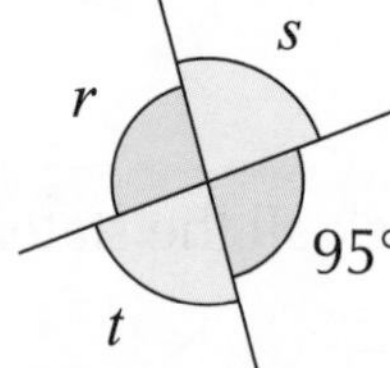

$r =$ .... °

$s =$ .... °

$t =$ .... °

3. Rahul is helping his cousin put together a circle that has been cut into five pieces (*A*, *B*, *C*, *D* and *E*). Piece *E* has gone missing.

You'll need to work out the angles inside the other pieces first.

Use the information below to work out the angle inside the missing piece *E*.

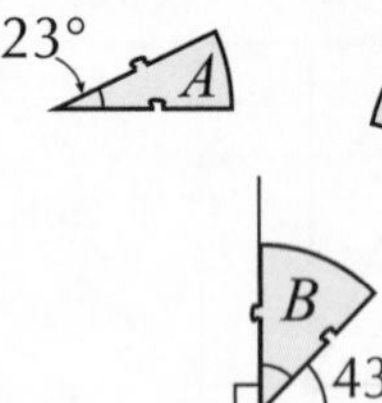
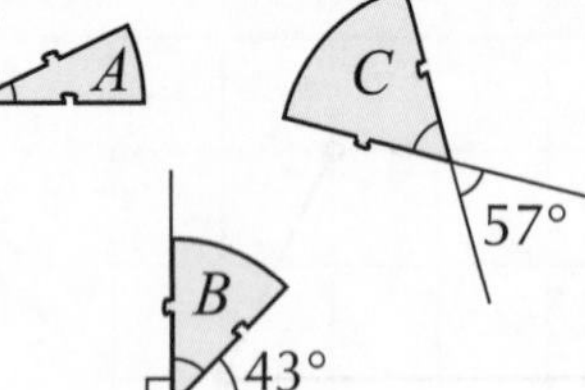

.... °

How did you do?

I agree with the title — angles rule! Oh, wait... Nothing too complicated here. Learn the rules and you're good to go. You should now be able to:

- [ ] **Use angle rules to find missing angles on a straight line.**
- [ ] **Use angle rules to find missing angles around a point.**

Angles in Triangles

None of the diagrams on this page are drawn accurately.

1. Find the missing angles.

a)

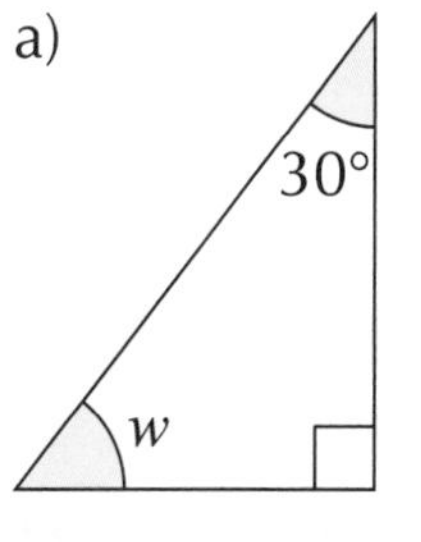

$w = \ldots\ldots\ldots\ldots ^\circ$

b)

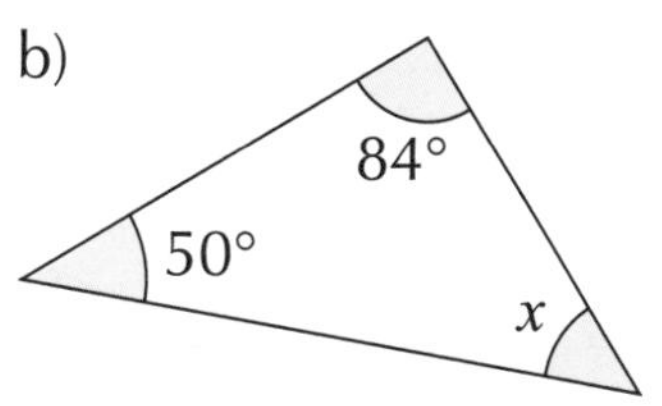

$x = \ldots\ldots\ldots\ldots ^\circ$

c)

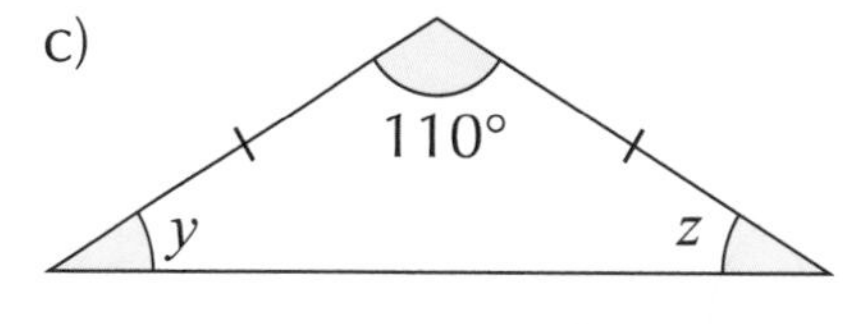

$y = \ldots\ldots\ldots\ldots ^\circ$

$z = \ldots\ldots\ldots\ldots ^\circ$

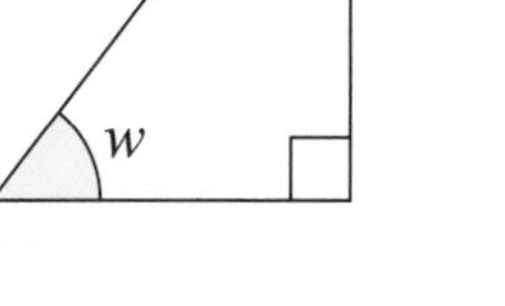

2. Work out the missing angles.

a)

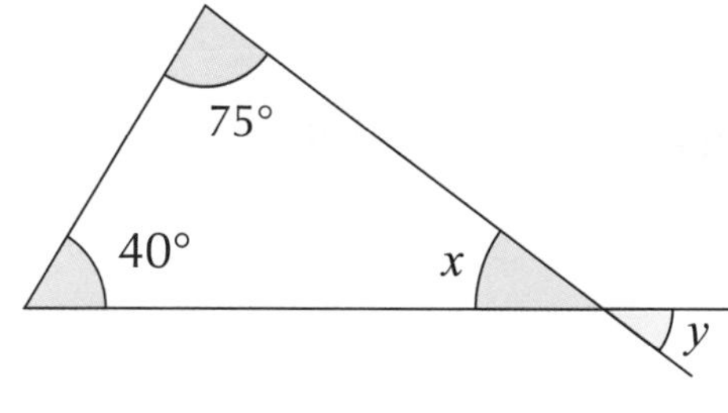

$x = \ldots\ldots\ldots\ldots ^\circ$

$y = \ldots\ldots\ldots\ldots ^\circ$

b)

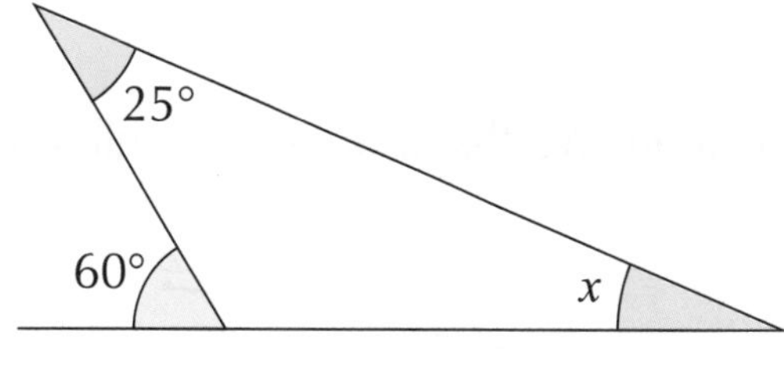

$x = \ldots\ldots\ldots\ldots ^\circ$

3. Aiesha has designed a logo for The Chips 'N' Dips Company. It is shown on the right.

The logo is made entirely from isosceles triangles.
Each one has the same internal angles. Work out the size of r.

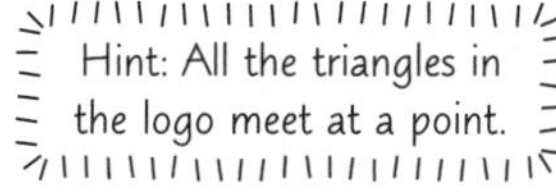

Hint: All the triangles in the logo meet at a point.

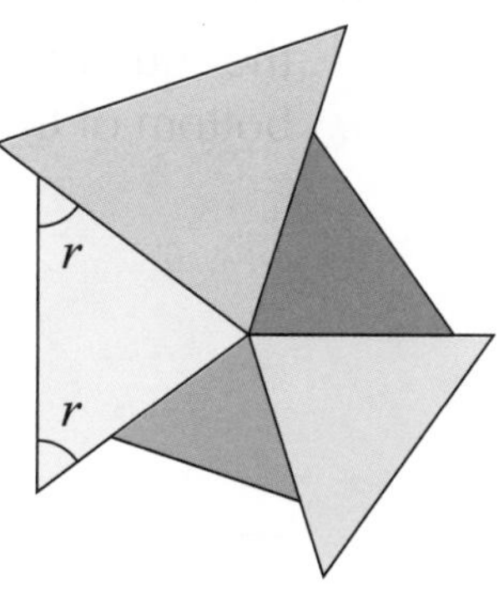

$r = \ldots\ldots\ldots\ldots ^\circ$

How did you do?

Some more triangle fun — now with added angles. After finishing this page, you should:

☐ **Be able to find a missing angle in a triangle using the sum of the angles.**

Measuring and Drawing Lines and Angles

1. Use a protractor to find the size of these angles.

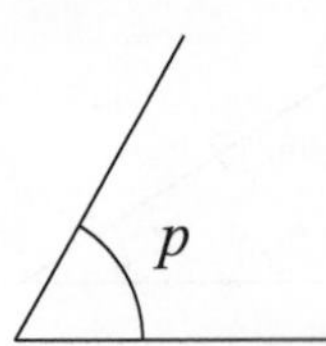

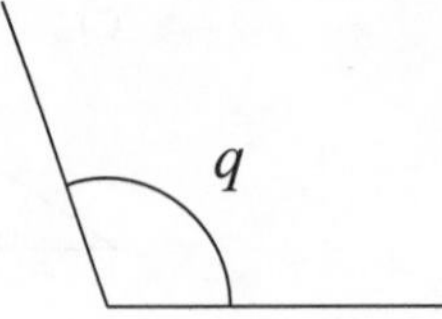

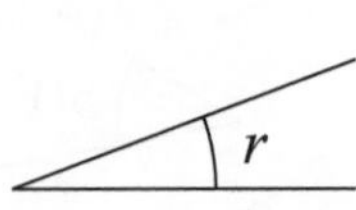

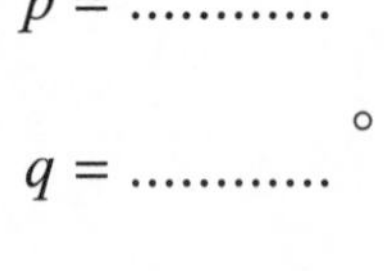

$p =$ .... °

$q =$ .... °

$r =$ .... °

2. For each of these shapes, circle the angle described and then measure it using a protractor.

a) The obtuse angle

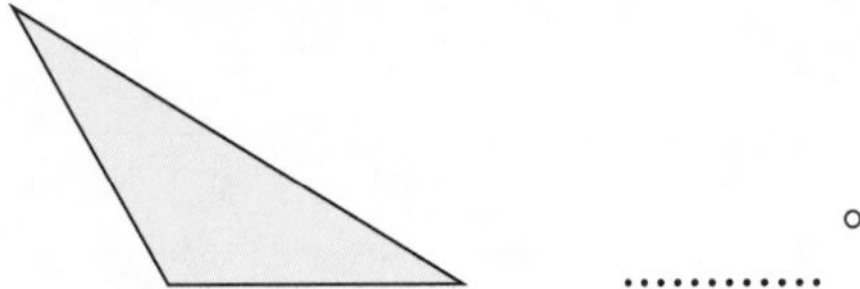

.... °

b) The acute angle

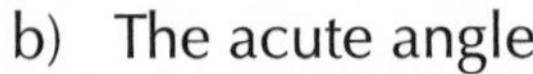
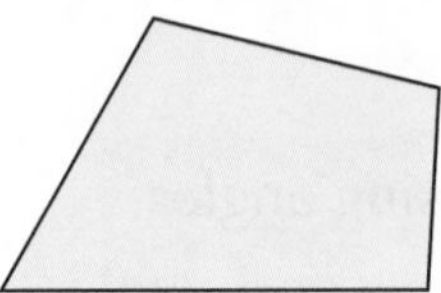

.... °

3. Draw a line *BC* that is 3 cm in length and makes an angle of 215° at *B*.

4. The Square Skate Squad have designed a miniature skate ramp.

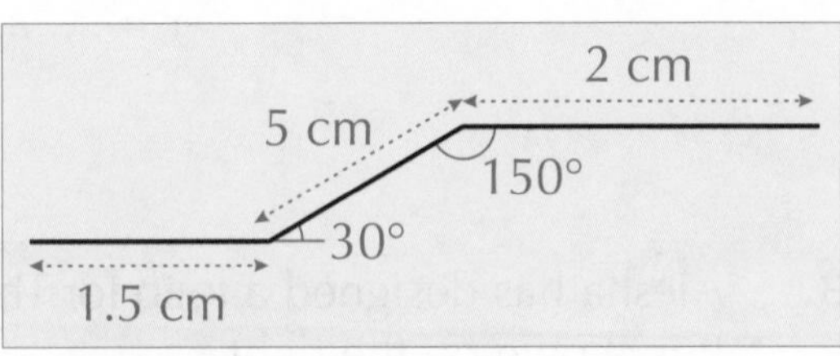

a) Use the sketch on the right to accurately draw the squad's ramp below. The platform at the bottom of the ramp has been drawn for you.

b) Use a ruler to measure the vertical height of the ramp. .... cm

How did you do?

Ahhh, nothing quite like the smell of sopping wet sheep and fresh cow dung in the morning. Hang on, this page is about using *protractors*?! ... My bad. Check you're now able to:

- ☐ **Use a ruler to measure line segments.**
- ☐ **Use a protractor to measure angles.**
- ☐ **Use a ruler to draw line segments.**
- ☐ **Use a ruler and protractor to draw angles.**

Constructing Triangles

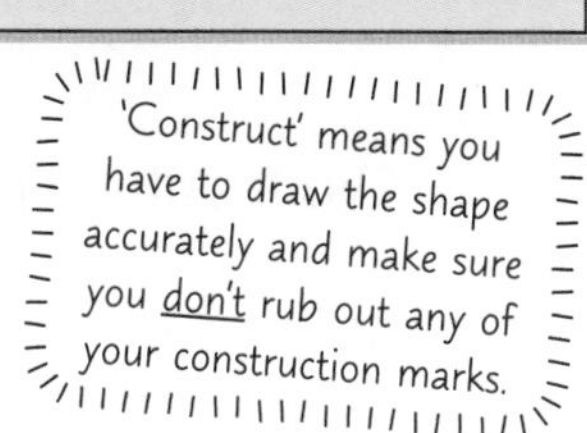

1. Construct triangle *ABC*, where *BAC* is 40° and *ABC* is 20°.

Use a ruler and a protractor. The line *AB* has been drawn for you.

A ——————— *B*

2. Construct the isosceles triangle *DEF*, where *DE* = 5 cm and *DEF* = 100°.

Use a ruler and a protractor. The line *EF* has been drawn for you.

3. Paul (*P*), Qiang (*Q*) and Ramesh (*R*) are sat around a campfire. Paul is sat 6 m from Qiang, Qiang is 4 m from Ramesh and Ramesh is 3 m from Paul.

Construct the triangle *PQR*. The line *PQ* has been drawn for you.
Use a ruler and a pair of compasses, and use a scale of 1 cm = 1 m.

How did you do?

Put down your hammer and nails and wipe your brow — that's enough constructing for the time being, phew! Before moving on to the next page, make sure you're able to:

- ☐ **Construct triangles when you're given two angles and one side.**
- ☐ **Construct triangles when you're given one angle and two sides.**
- ☐ **Construct triangles when you're given three sides.**

Perimeter

1. Work out the perimeter of the following shapes.

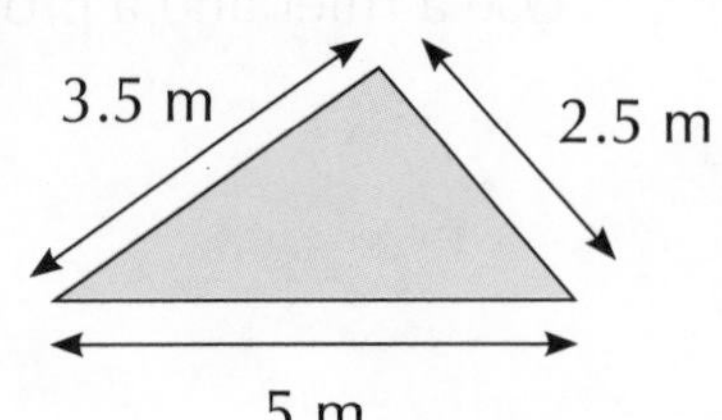

a)

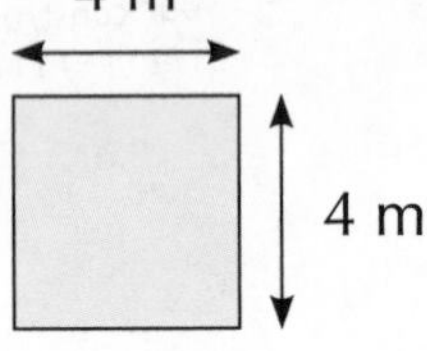

.... m

b)

.... m

c)

.... m

2. Find the perimeter of each of these regular shapes.

a)

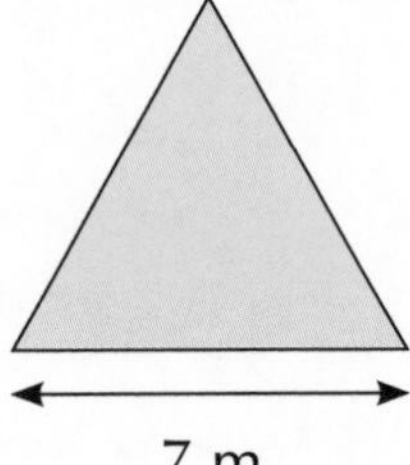

.... m

b)

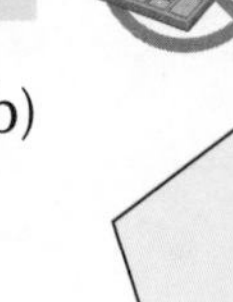

.... m

3. Jackie has shaded a shape on a grid.
Calculate the perimeter of the shape.

The grid is made up of 1 cm² squares.

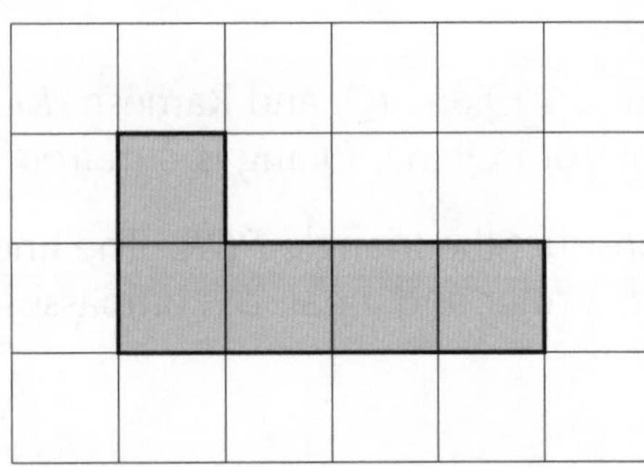

.... cm

4. Use the perimeters of these shapes to work out the lengths of the missing sides.

a) Perimeter = 21 m

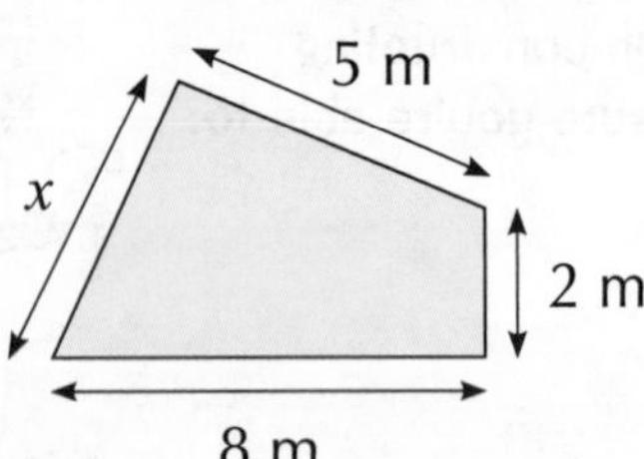

x = ... m

b) Perimeter = 25 m

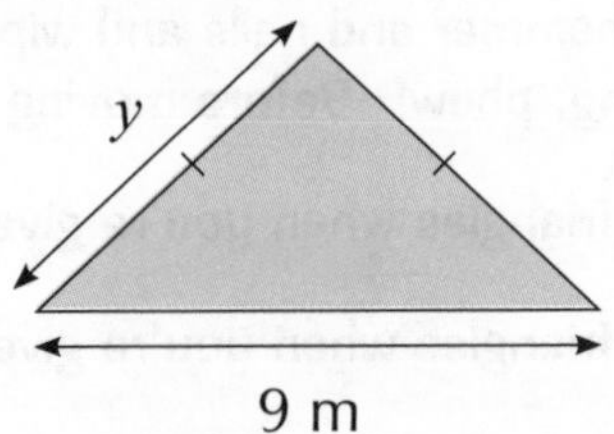

y = ... m

Perimeter

5. Find the perimeter of the following shapes.

None of the diagrams on this page are drawn accurately.

a)

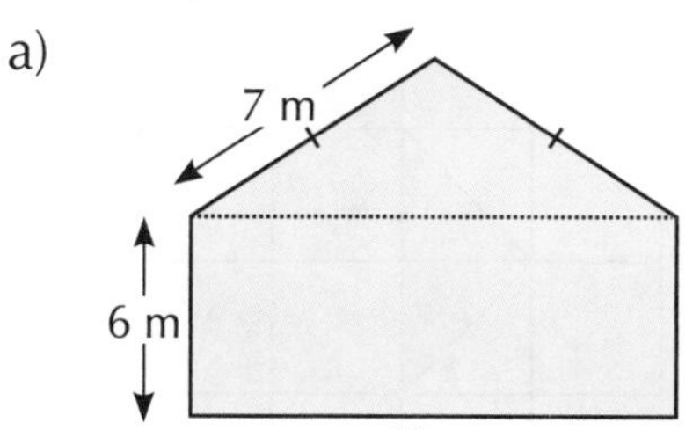

.... m

b)

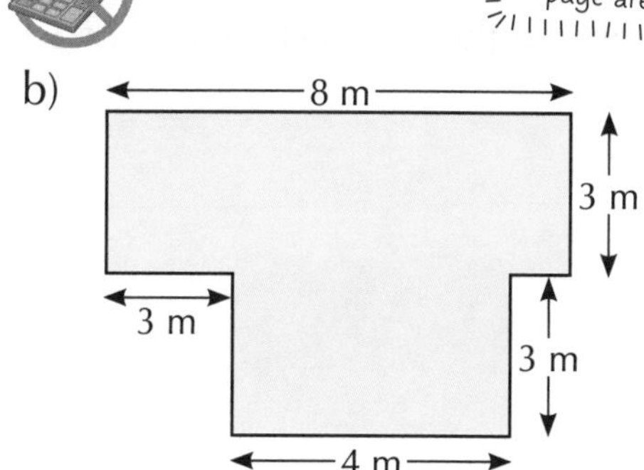

.... m

6. Lila has cut the shape of a house out of a square sheet of paper.

a) Calculate the perimeter of the house.

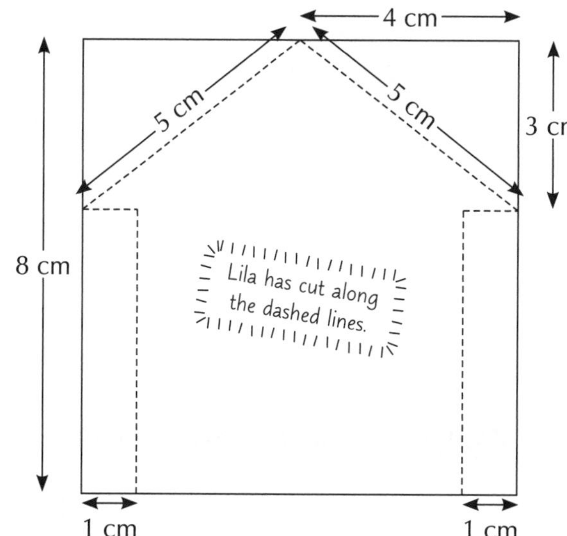

.... cm

b) Lila adds a rectangular piece of paper to the side of the house to make a garage, as shown on the right. What is the total perimeter of the house and garage?

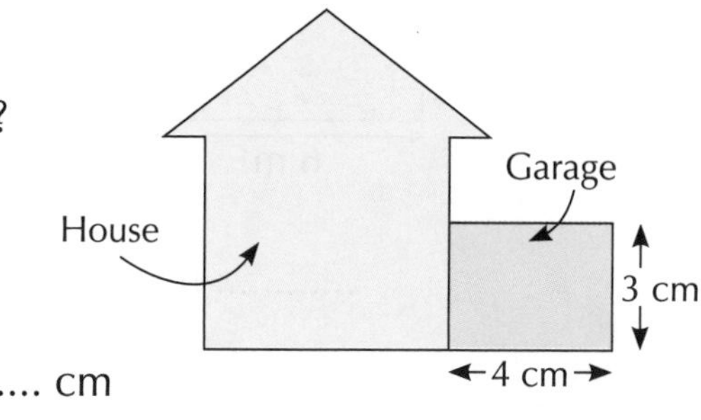

.... cm

How did you do?

It's easy to lose track of which sides you've counted when finding a perimeter. Top tip — mark where you start counting from, then you won't end up counting the same side twice. See if you now can:

☐ Find the perimeter of a given shape. ☐ Solve problems involving the perimeter of a shape.

Area

1. Work out the area of the shaded shape on this grid. Each square on the grid has an area of 1 cm².

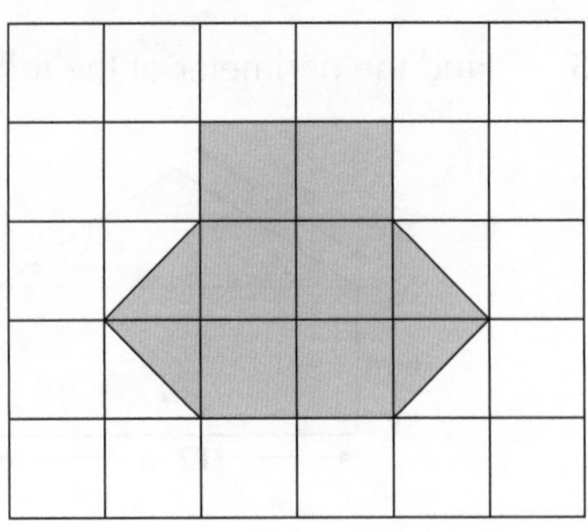

.... cm²

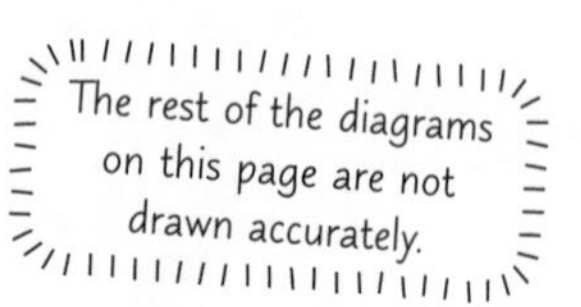

2. Find the area of each shape.

a)

.... m²

b)

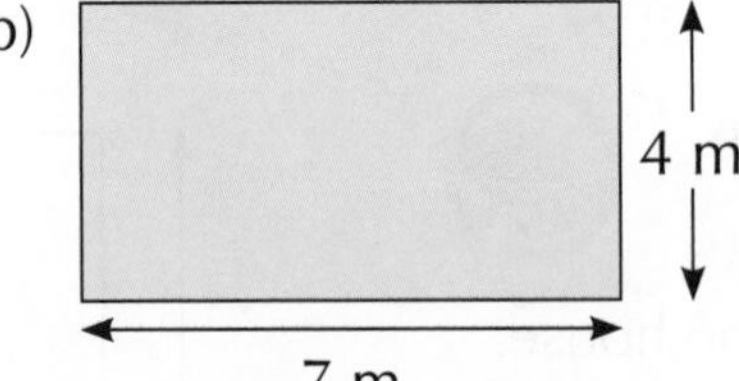

.... m²

c)

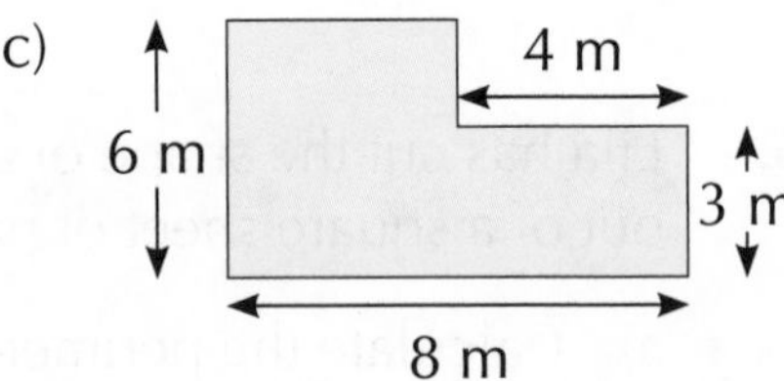

.... m²

3. Work out the area of each triangle.

a)

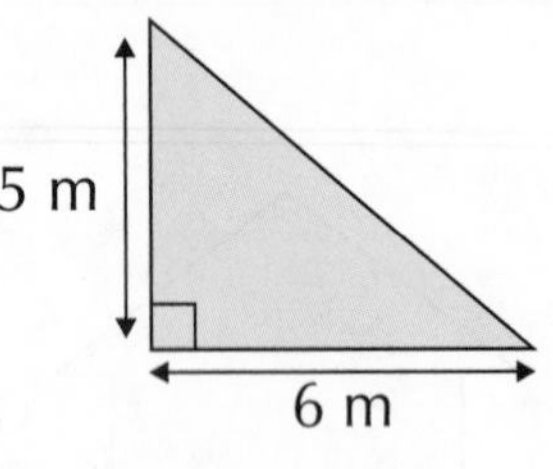

.... m²

b)

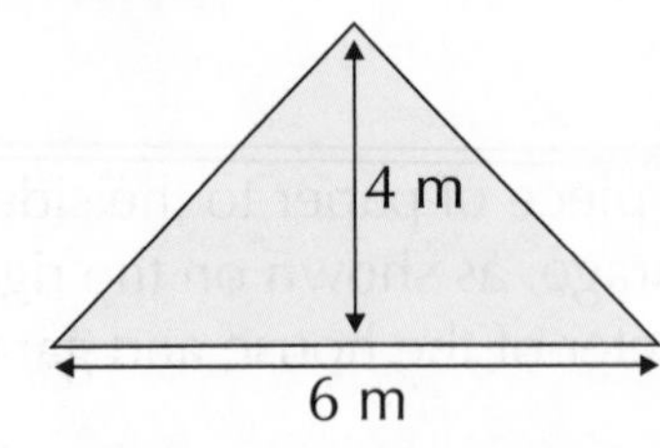

.... m²

c)

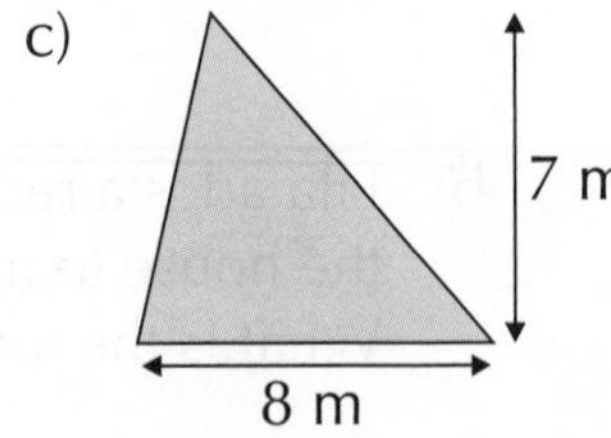

.... m²

4. The area of each of these shapes is 64 m². Find the missing lengths.

a)

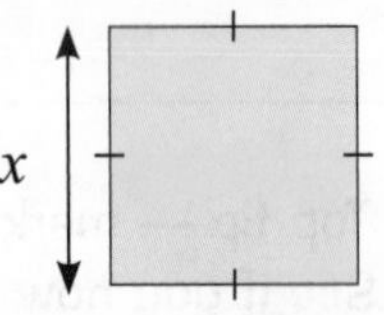

$x =$ .... m

b)

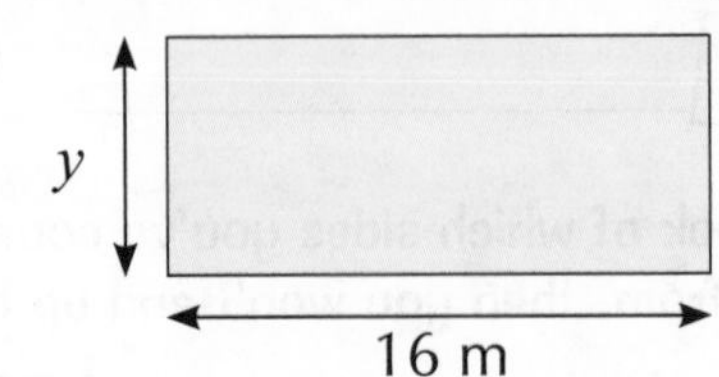

$y =$ .... m

Area

5. Here is part of a signpost. Work out its area.

None of the diagrams on this page are drawn accurately.

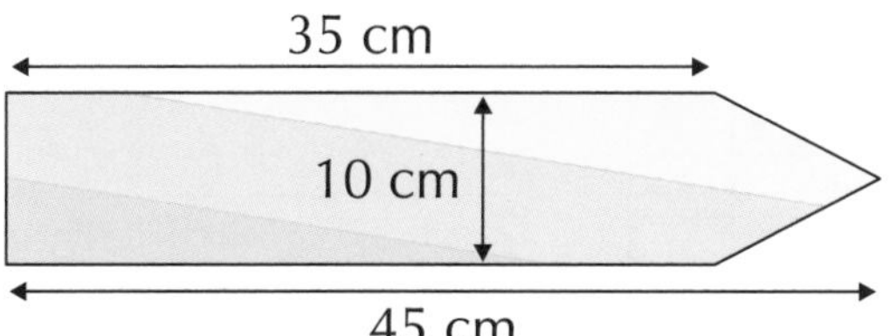

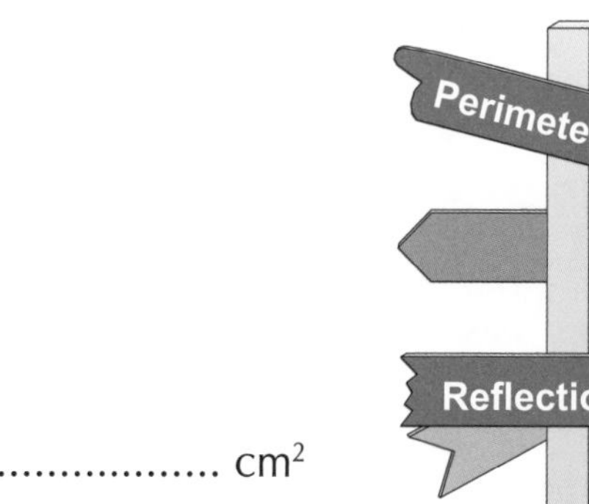

.... cm^2

6. Clayton has written a letter on a square piece of paper with a width of 12 cm. He has a rectangular envelope with an area of 176 cm^2 and a width of 16 cm.

Can Clayton's letter fit into the envelope without folding the paper? Explain your reasoning.

....

....

7. Casey is buying a particularly ugly rug for her bedroom, as shown on the right. The rug is made from the right-angled and equilateral triangular pieces below.

Work out the total area of the rug.

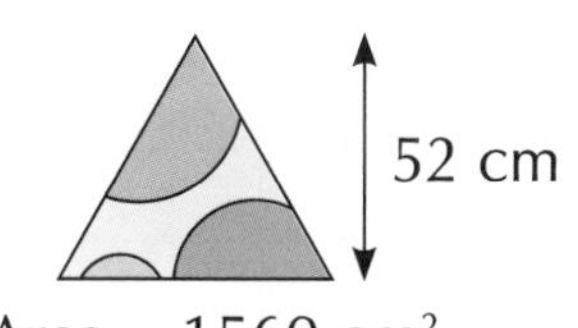

.... cm^2

How did you do?

'Composite' shapes are shapes that are made by joining more than one basic shape — e.g. the signpost above is a composite shape made from a rectangle and a triangle. Now, make sure you can:

☐ Calculate the area of squares and rectangles.

☐ Calculate the area of triangles.

☐ Calculate the area of composite shapes made up from squares, rectangles and triangles.

Reflection

1. Reflect shape A in the mirror line. Label the new shape B.

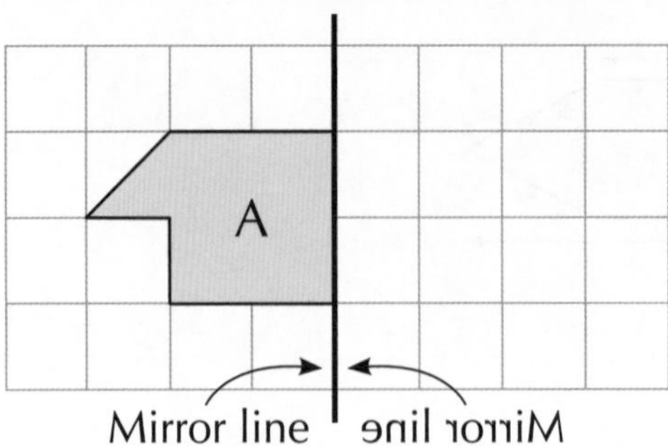

2. Reflect each of these shapes in the given mirror line.

a)

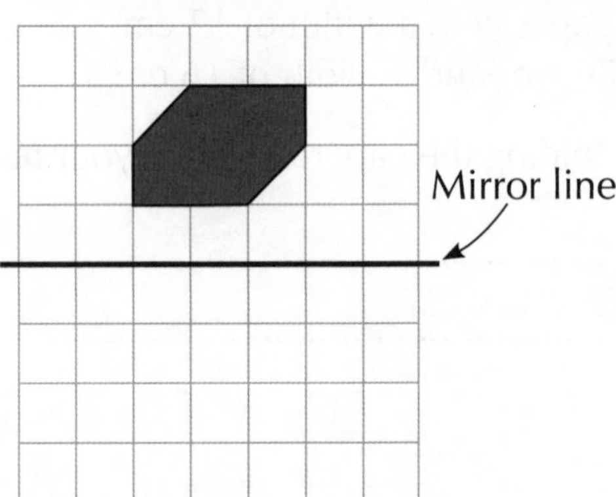

b)

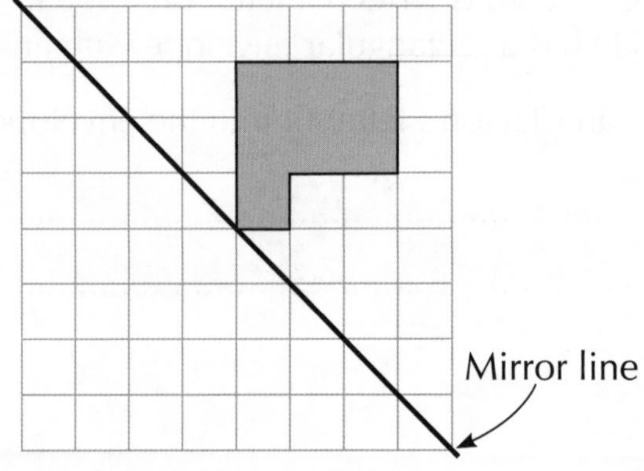

3. Five points have been plotted on the axes on the right.

a) What point is obtained by reflecting A in the x-axis?

Tick your answer: ☐ B ☐ C ☐ D ☐ E

b) Draw the triangle ACD and then draw its reflection in the y-axis.

c) The point E is reflected in the x-axis and then in the y-axis. What are its new coordinates?

(........., ...)

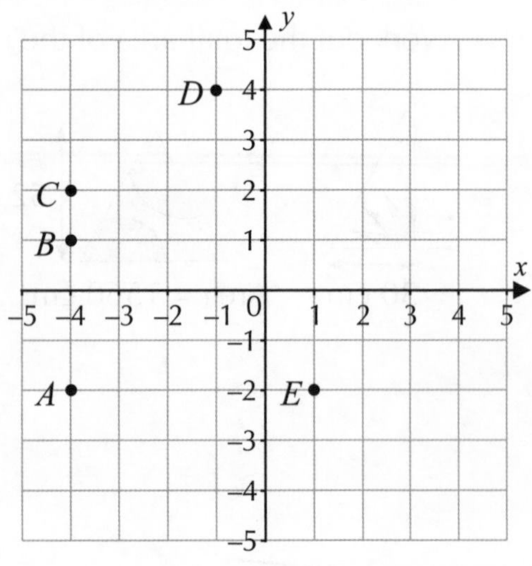

How did you do?

Well done, you've completed the page on reflections! Look in a mirror and you'll see a champion!
What do you mean you'll need a mirror to read that? Check to see if you can now:

☐ **Reflect shapes on grids and axes in horizontal, vertical and diagonal mirror lines.**

3D Shapes

1. Write the name under each of the 3D shapes below.

a) 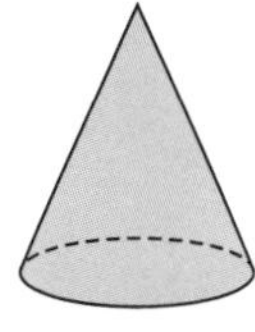

....

b) 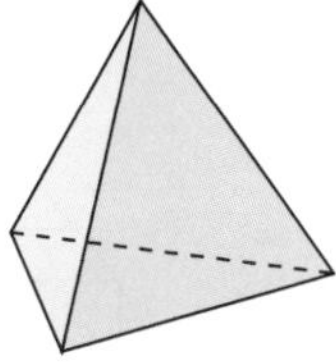

....

c) 

....

2. Fill in the table below to describe the 3D shapes.

	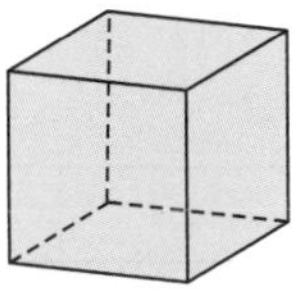 Cube	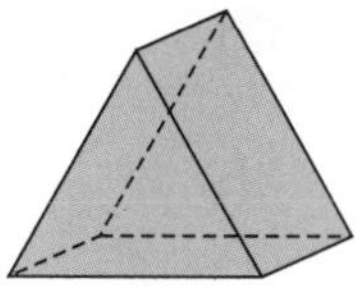	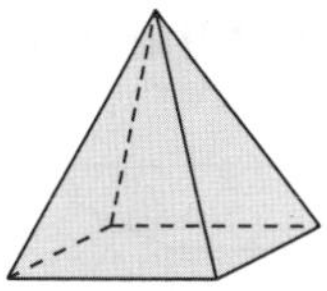 Square-based Pyramid	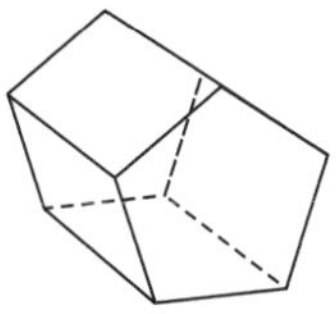 Pentagonal Prism
Name	Cube	....	Square-based Pyramid	Pentagonal Prism
Faces	....	....	....	....
Vertices	8	....	....	....
Edges	....	9	....	....

3. Circle the prisms in the collection of 3D shapes below.

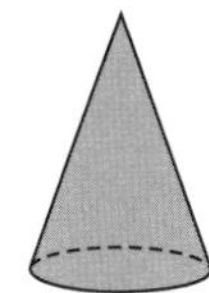
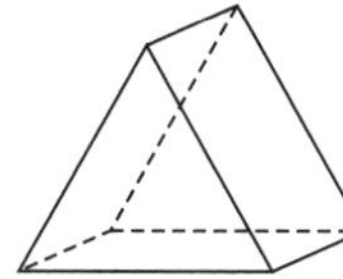
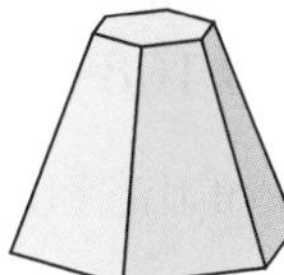

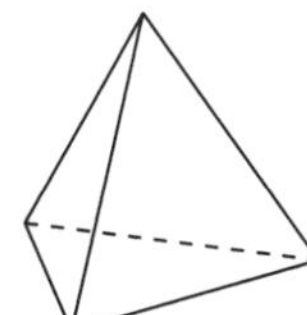

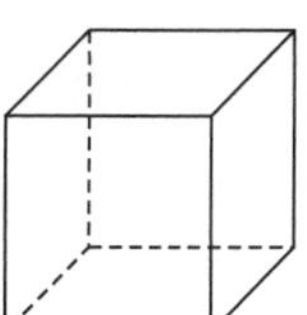

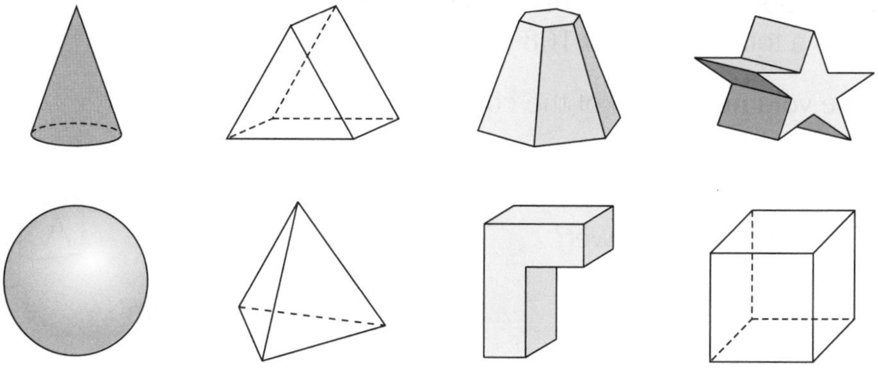

How did you do?

3D shapes are great — they always add another dimension to any maths question. Once you've finished this page, have a think about what you feel confident about. You should be able to:

☐ Name and identify 3D shapes. ☐ Give the number of edges, vertices and faces of 3D shapes.

Volume

1. These shapes are made from blocks with a volume 1 cm³. Find the volume of each shape.

a)

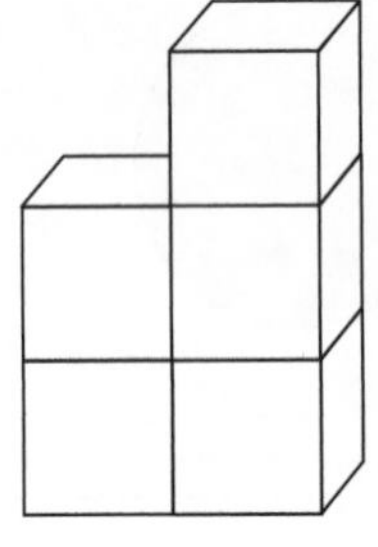

.... cm³

b)

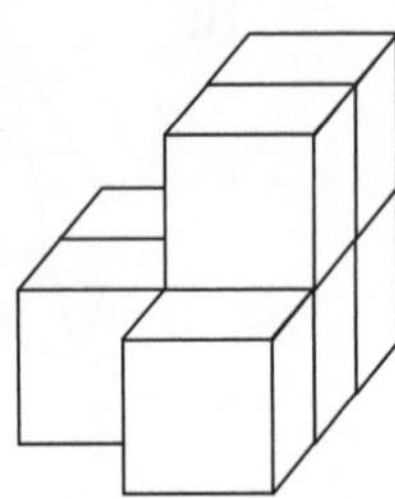

.... cm³

2. Work out the volume of the following cuboids.

a)

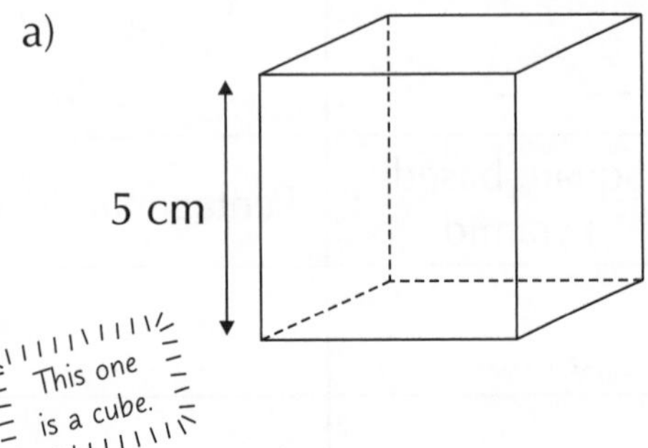

.... cm³

b)

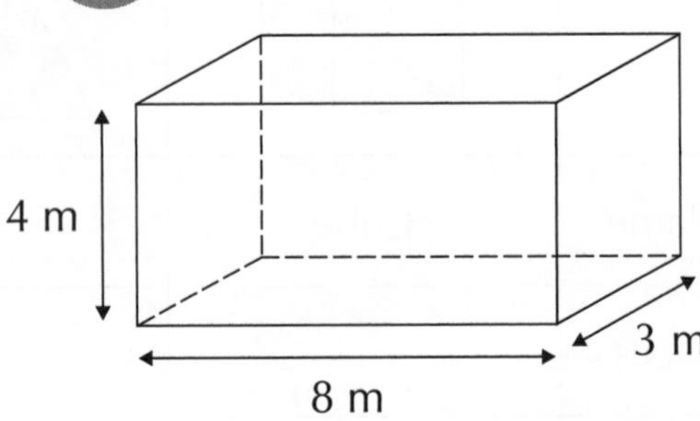

.... m³

3. Colm has a collection of alphabet cubes. They each have the same volume.

He stacks some cubes to spell out his name, making a tower that has a total volume of 108 cm³.

a) What is the volume of each of the cubes?

.... cm³

b) What is the height of the tower?

.... cm

C O L M

How did you do?

Last page, hurrah... but keep the volume down would you — I'm trying to sneak in a quick nap before the Review Exercise on the next page. One last time then, by now you should be able to:

☐ Find the volume of shapes made from cubes. ☐ Calculate the volume of cubes and cuboids.

☐  ☐  ☐

Section Four — Review Exercise

So that's it — you've reached the end of the section. Give yourself a pat on the back. Then gear yourself up for these review questions to test whether or not you know it all.

1. Shape A has been drawn on the grid below.

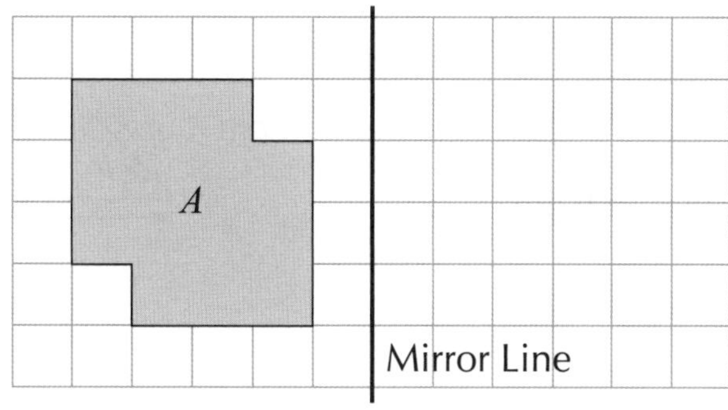

a) (i) How many lines of symmetry does shape A have?

.... 1 mark

(ii) What is the order of rotational symmetry of shape A?

.... 1 mark

b) Reflect shape A in the mirror line. Label it B.

1 mark

2. Camille has a swimming pool in her garden. The diagram below is an overhead view of the pool. It is not accurately drawn.

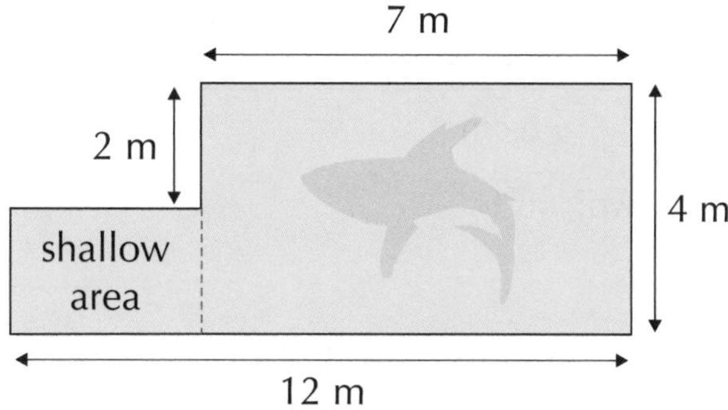

a) (i) Find the perimeter of the swimming pool.

.... m 1 mark

(ii) What is the area of the pool's surface?

.... m^2 2 marks

b) The pool is 1 m deep in the shallow area and 2 m deep everywhere else. What is the volume of the swimming pool?

.... m^3 2 marks

Section Four — Review Exercise

3. Look at the diagram on the right.

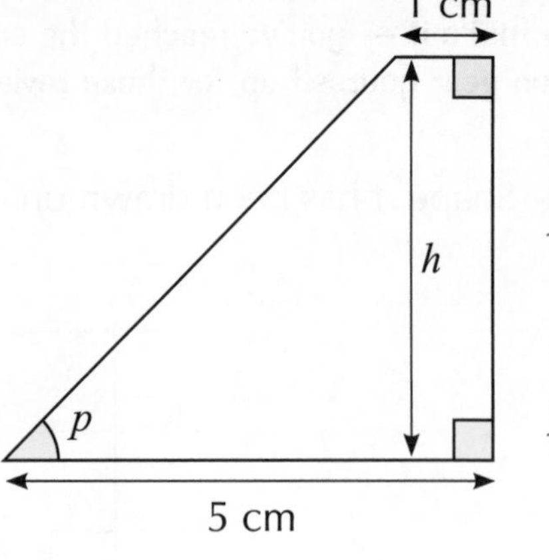

a) What is the quadrilateral in the diagram called?

.... 1 mark

b) (i) Use a ruler to measure the height of the shape, h.

h = ... cm 1 mark

(ii) Calculate the area of the shape.

.... cm^2 2 marks

c) Use a protractor to find the size of the angle p.

p = ...° 1 mark

d) The shape is a cross-section of a prism. Complete the following sentence.

The prism has .... faces, ... vertices and .... edges. 2 marks

4. Look at the triangle below. It is not accurately drawn.

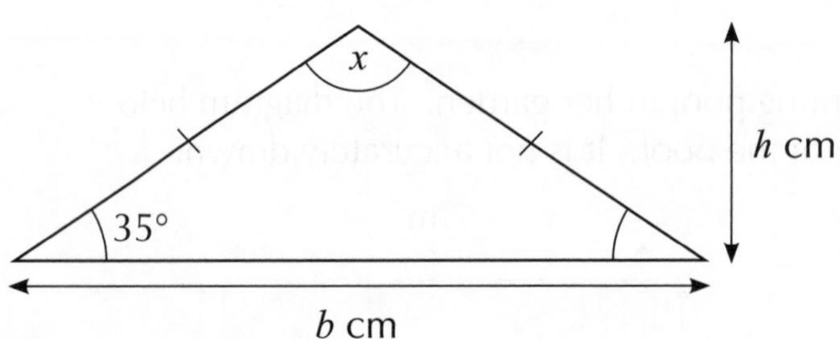

a) What type of triangle is shown?

.... 1 mark

b) Find the size of the angle x. Do **not** use a protractor.

...........° 2 marks

c) The area of the triangle is 9 cm^2. The base (b) and height (h) are whole numbers. Write down two different combinations of b and h.

b = ... cm and h = ... cm or b = ... cm and h = ... cm 2 marks

It's all shaping up rather nicely...

Well done, you've made it to the end of another section. Take a break, mark the Review Exercise and make a note of anything you struggled with. Once you feel happy with everything here, you can call yourself a geometer extraordinaire (which means you're ace at shapes — smashing).

Score: 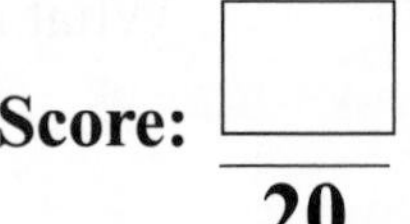

Section Five — Probability and Statistics

This section is all about probability (working out how likely things are to happen) and statistics (working with data). Run through the questions below to see how confident you are before you make a start.

Before you Start

1. Which of these things do you think is the most likely to happen? Tick one box.

☐ The Moon will fall out of the sky.

☐ You will have to go to school on Sunday.

☐ A baby will be born somewhere in the world today.

2. A fair coin is tossed. How likely do you think it is that the coin will land on heads? Circle your answer.

Impossible　　Unlikely　　Evens　　Likely　　Certain

3. The table below shows the number of people who visited a fairground on different days of the week.

	Thursday	Friday	Saturday	Sunday
Number of people	1456	1987	2641	2450

a) How many people visited the fairground on Sunday?

....

b) On which day of the week did the fewest people visit the fairground?

....

4. The graph on the right shows the temperature of the inside of a car on a hot day. What is the temperature of the car after...

15 minutes? .... °C

30 minutes? .... °C

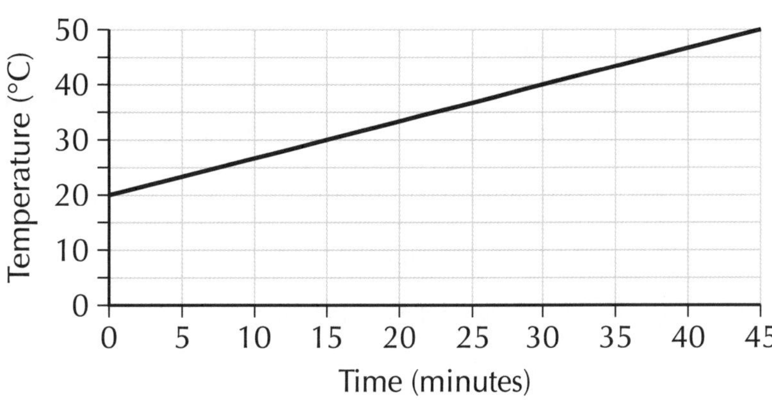

Probability

1. Five events are written below, along with five words that describe how likely things are to happen.

Match each event with its description by drawing straight lines between them.

There will be fewer than 30 days in February.		Certain
You will find a giraffe in your street tomorrow.		Likely
It will rain while you're outside at some point in the next year.		Evens
You will pick a red ball from a bag containing only 5 red and 5 blue balls.		Unlikely
You will develop X-ray vision by correctly answering this question.		Impossible

2. Kelly asks the five people in her office how they got to work. Four of them got a bus, but the bus was late for two of these people. All five of them managed to arrive at work on time.

Kelly picks someone at random from the five people in her office.

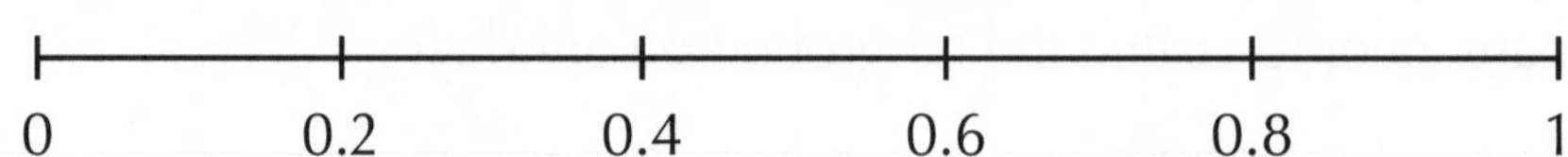

a) Write A on the line above to show the probability that the person she picks got a bus.

b) Write B on the line above to show the probability that the person she picks got a bus that was late.

c) Write C on the line above to show the probability that the person she picks arrived on time.

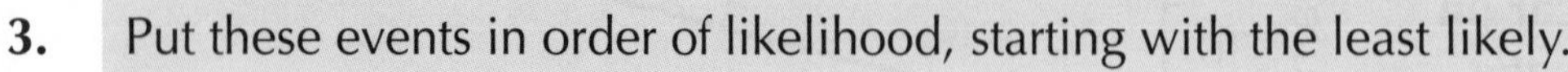

3. Put these events in order of likelihood, starting with the least likely.

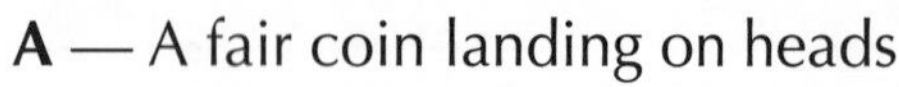

A — A fair coin landing on heads

B — The spinner on the right landing on R

C — A fair dice, labelled 1-6, landing on a 7

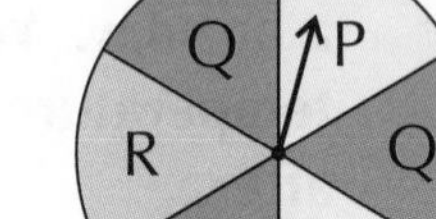

.... , ... , ...

Probability

4. There are 10 tickets, numbered 1-10, in a raffle. The winning ticket is drawn at random.

Find, as a fraction in its simplest form, the probability that:

a) the winning ticket is 6

....

b) the winning ticket is even

....

c) the winning ticket is odd and less than 5

....

5. The probability that Nathan goes for a walk on Monday is 0.2.

a) What is the probability that Nathan doesn't go for a walk on Monday?

....

b) Nathan decides to go for a walk on Tuesday. He either walks to the beach, the park or the river. The probability that he walks to the beach is 0.4 and the probability that he walks to the park is 0.1. What is the probability that he walks to the river?

....

6. There are 80 jars of jam on a market stall. 10 of the jars contain apricot jam, 25 contain strawberry jam and the rest contain raspberry jam. The stall owner picks a jar at random.

a) What is the probability that the jar contains either apricot or strawberry jam?

....

b) What is the probability that the jar doesn't contain apricot jam?

....

c) What is the probability that the jar contains blackberry jam?

....

How did you do?

So that's probability covered — what are the chances that you breezed through it? Before moving on, have a think about what you've just achieved. You should:

- ☐ **Be able to describe the likelihood of events.**
- ☐ **Understand the 0-1 probability scale.**
- ☐ **Know that the probabilities of all possible outcomes add up to 1.**
- ☐ **Be able to calculate the probability of events based on equally likely outcomes.**

 ☐  ☐  ☐

Tables, Bar Charts and Pictograms

1. The table on the right shows the amount of spaghetti eaten by the competitors in the National Spaghetti Eating Championships 2019.

Name	Amount eaten
Ana	555 g
Bryn	189 g
Cam	464 g
Davood	651 g
Elijah	548 g

a) Who ate the most spaghetti?

....

b) What was the total amount of spaghetti eaten by all five of the competitors?

.... g

c) How much more spaghetti did Ana eat than Bryn?

.... g

2. A teacher asks a group of pupils to name their favourite flower. The results are shown in the table.

Flower	Daisy	Daffodil	Lily	Rose	Violet
Number of pupils	4	???	12	6	24

An incomplete bar chart is drawn below.

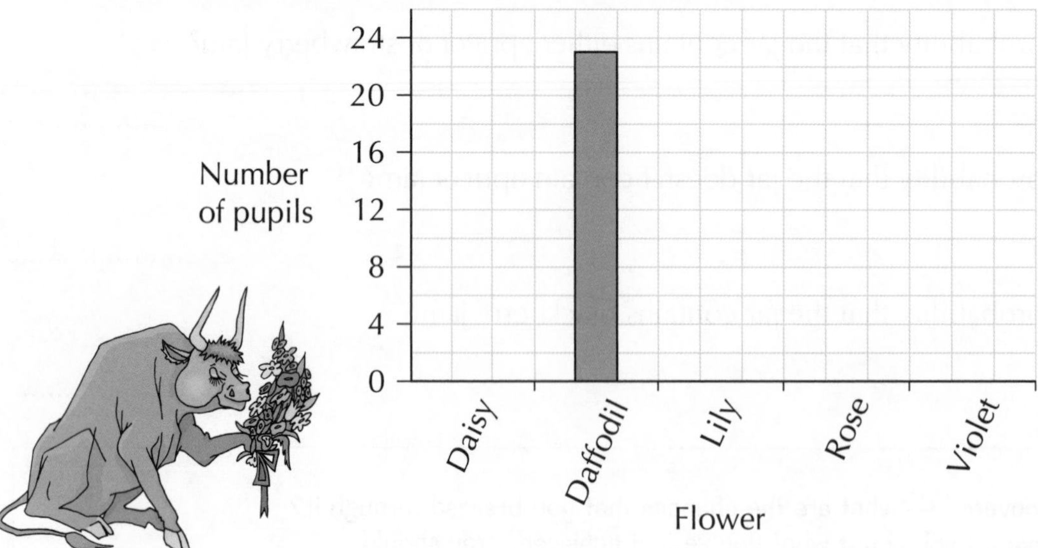

a) Complete the bar chart for the remaining four flowers.

b) How many pupils said that daffodils were their favourite type of flower?

....

Tables, Bar Charts and Pictograms

3. Cindy picks a series of cards from a deck and writes down the suit of each card (♣, ♠, ♦ or ♥). The results are shown below.

a) Complete this table to show the number of times she picked each suit from the deck.

Suit	♣	♠	♦	♥
Tally				
Frequency	....	....	....	....

b) What fraction of the cards picked were hearts?
Give your answer in its simplest form.

....

4. An estate agent constructs a pictogram to show the prices at which 50 houses were sold in the last six months.

a) The estate agent sold 8 houses in the price range £100 000-£149 999.
Complete the pictogram.

Price	
Less than £100 000	
£100 000-£149 999	
£150 000-£199 999	
£200 000-£249 999	
£250 000 or more	

Key: ☐ = 4 houses

b) How many houses were sold for less than £100 000?

....

c) What percentage of the 50 houses were sold for £200 000 or more?

.... %

Tables, Bar Charts and Pictograms

5. The dual bar chart below shows the number of sightings of talking snowmen in two countries over a number of years.

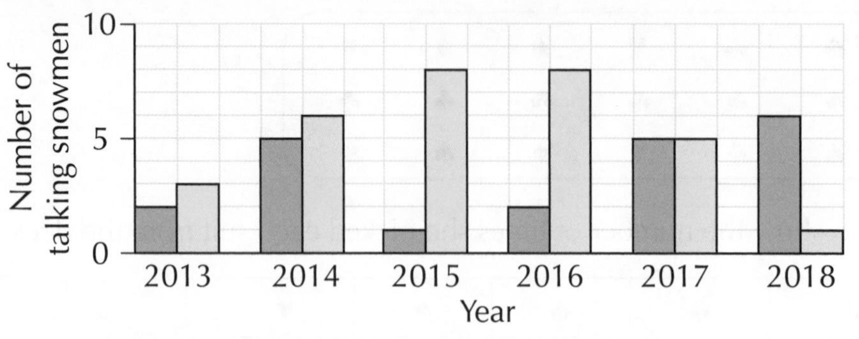

a) In how many years were there more sightings of talking snowmen in the UK than in Denmark? ....

b) Calculate how many more sightings of talking snowmen there have been in Denmark than in the UK in the years 2016-2018.

....

c) In the space below, construct a pictogram to show the number of sightings of talking snowmen in the UK. Represent two snowmen using this symbol: ◯

d) Bjørn says that the number of sightings each year of talking snowmen in Denmark is increasing. Do you agree? Explain your answer.

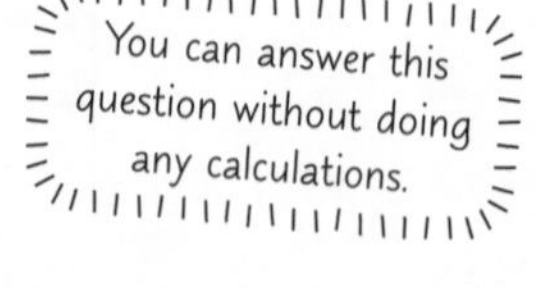

....

....

How did you do?

Lots of charts and diagrams on the last few pages — I hope you sharpened your pencil before you set off. Tick off these points to make sure you've got to grips with it all. You should be able to:

- ☐ **Interpret and construct tables and frequency tables.**
- ☐ **Interpret and construct pictograms.**
- ☐ **Interpret and construct bar charts, including dual bar charts.**

 ☐  ☐  ☐

Pie Charts

1. A group of mathematicians were asked to name their favourite type of chart. The results are shown in the pie chart below.

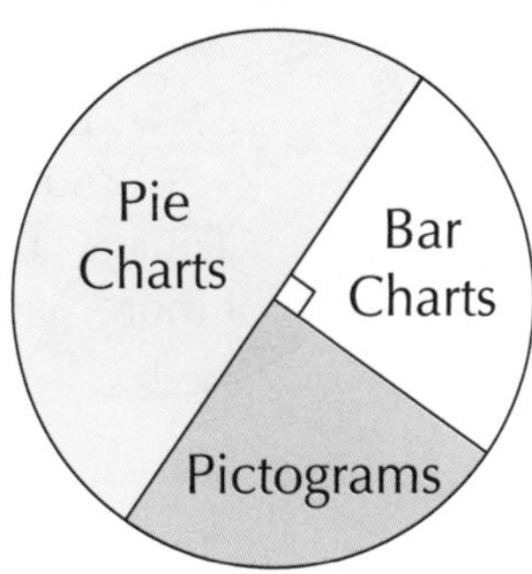

a) What percentage of the mathematicians said that pie charts are their favourite type of chart?

.... %

b) There are 56 mathematicians in the group. How many of them said that bar charts are their favourite?

....

2. Taylor has a gem collection. The proportion of each type of gem in the collection is shown by this pie chart.

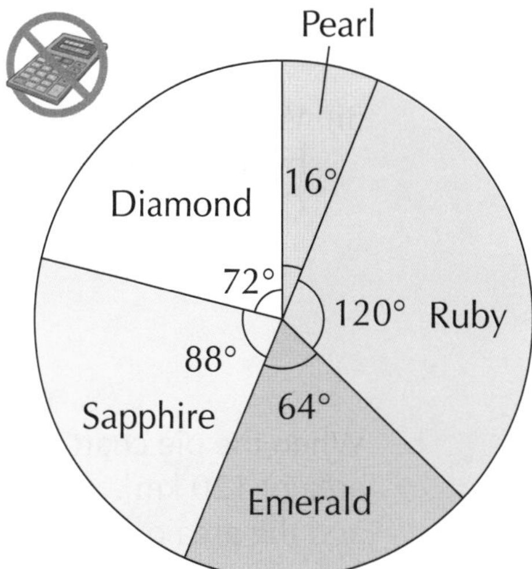

a) Which type of gem does Taylor have fewest of?

....

b) 15 of the gems are rubies. How many gems does Taylor have in total? Circle your answer.

Use the pie chart to work out what fraction of the gems are rubies.

30 45 60 120

3. A grid is split into 60 identical squares. 15 of the squares are shaded red, 25 are shaded blue and the rest are shaded yellow.

Complete the table below. Then use it to sketch a pie chart showing the proportion of the grid that is shaded each of the colours.

Label the angles on your diagram.

Colour	Number of squares	Angle
Red	15	....
Blue	....	....
Yellow	....	....

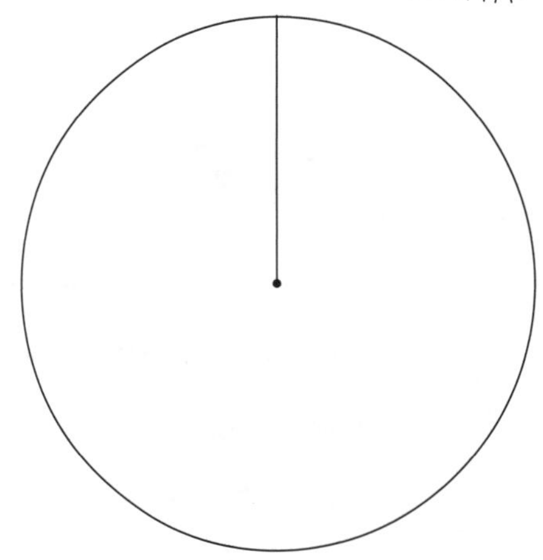

Pie Charts

4. The pie chart on the right shows the number of plays that the people in an acting group have been cast in since they joined the group.

Explain why you cannot calculate the number of people who have been cast in three plays.

....

....

5. A town is divided into four districts — housing, commercial, industry and green space. The pie chart below has been drawn accurately to show this.

a) (i) What is the angle of the industry sector?

...............°

(ii) What fraction of the town is taken up by the industry district?
Give your answer in its simplest form.

....

b) When the pie chart was constructed, the town had a total land area of 120 km². Over the next five years, the town expanded and the area of land covered by the industry district doubled.

(i) Calculate the area of land taken up by the industry district now.

.... km²

(ii) A new pie chart is to be constructed to account for the expansion. The total land area of the town is now 180 km². Calculate the angle of the industry sector.

..................°

How did you do?

My, my — I'm mighty peckish after thinking of all that pie. Before raiding the fridge, you should:

- ☐ Know that pie charts show proportions.
- ☐ Be able to interpret pie charts.
- ☐ Be able to construct pie charts accurately.
- ☐ Be able to find the number of items represented by a sector of a pie chart.

Mean, Median, Mode and Range

1. Look at this list of numbers: 5, 7, 3, 4, 6, 3, 2

a) Which of the numbers is the mode?

....

b) (i) Put the numbers in order, starting with the smallest.

....

(ii) Calculate the range of the numbers.

....

(iii) What is the median of the numbers?

....

2. The box below shows how many training sessions each of the members of a goalball club have attended in the last year.

32	40	25	12
9	48	27	15

a) Add up all of the numbers.

....

b) Find the mean number of training sessions attended.

....

3. Harvey counts how many light bulbs there are in each room of his house. The results are: 4, 3, 1, 2, 1, 1

a) Find the range of this data.

....

b) Complete each of these sentences by using the words on the right.

Median

Mode Mean

(i) The .... of the numbers is 2.

(ii) The .... of the numbers is 1.5.

Mean, Median, Mode and Range

4. Priti weighs six conkers that she collected from the park. The masses, in grams, are shown on the right.

3.2	6.8	7.2
5.3	4.4	5.5

a) Find the mean mass.

.... g

b) (i) What is the range of Priti's data?

.... g

(ii) The conker that Priti recorded as having a mass of 3.2 g was weighed incorrectly. The actual mass of this conker is between 3.2 g and 7.2 g. How would using the actual mass affect the range? Explain your answer.

....

....

5. Rachel asks a group of people at the library how long it took them to travel there. The responses are shown below.

32 minutes 45 minutes 1 hour 26 minutes 15 minutes

a) What was the median time? Circle your answer above.

b) (i) Find the mean time taken to travel to the library, to the nearest minute.

.... minutes

(ii) Rachel asks a different group of people the same question. She finds that the mean time taken to travel to the library for that group is 40 minutes.

Using the means, compare the time it took the second group to travel to the library with the time it took the first group.

....

....

How did you do?

The average person really loves answering questions on the mean, median, mode and range — but I'm afraid those questions are all done with for the moment. Moving on then, you should be able to:

☐ **Calculate the mean, median and mode of a set of data.**

☐ **Calculate the range of a set of data.**

Section Five — Review Exercise

So that's Section Five all wrapped up. Well, apart from these review questions, that is. They'll really test if you've got to grips with all that probability and stats. Off you go.

1. A group of teenagers are on a school trip in the countryside. They check the signal strength on their phones and record the number of bars of signal in this pictogram.

Bars of signal	
None	
1	
2	
3	
4+	

Key: ▮▮▮▮ = 4 phones

a) How many phones have exactly one bar of signal?

.... 1 mark

b) One of the teenagers is picked at random from the group. Put a cross (X) on this line to mark the probability of this teenager's phone having exactly one bar of signal.

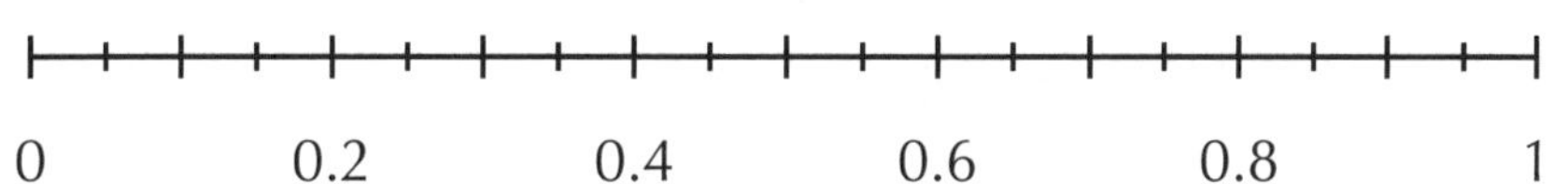

1 mark

2. A shoe shop records the shoe size of eight people who visit the shop. The results are shown below.

8 6 10 10 12 9 9 8

a) Find:

(i) the median shoe size,

.... 1 mark

(ii) the mean shoe size.

.... 2 marks

b) A frequency table for all 1056 visitors to the shoe shop in a year is given below.

Shoe size	6	7	8	9	10	11	12
Frequency	174	134	231	253	115	98	51

What fraction of the visitors had a shoe size greater than 9?
Give your answer in its simplest form.

.... 2 marks

Section Five — Review Exercise

3. A shepherd has 72 sheep in her flock, each of which is marked with dye. Half of the flock are marked with green dye, 16 are marked with red dye and the rest are marked with yellow dye.

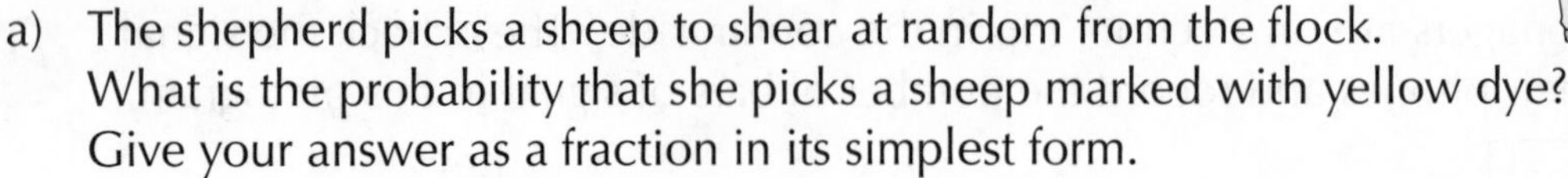

a) The shepherd picks a sheep to shear at random from the flock. What is the probability that she picks a sheep marked with yellow dye? Give your answer as a fraction in its simplest form.

.... 2 marks

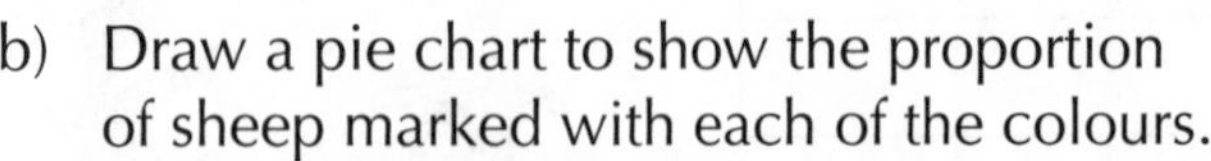

b) Draw a pie chart to show the proportion of sheep marked with each of the colours.

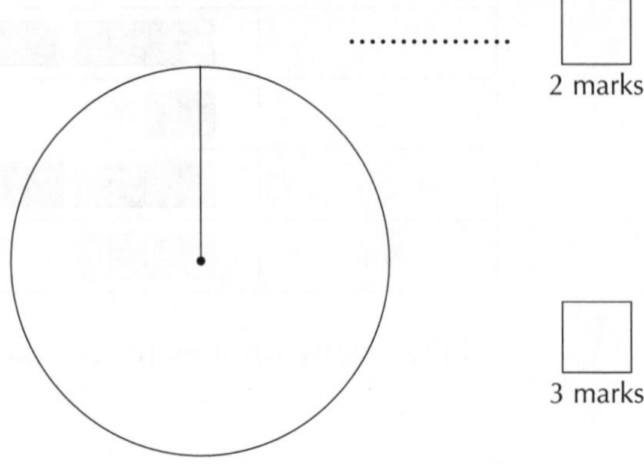

3 marks

4. A bakery sells loaves, cakes, pies and biscuits. The bar chart on the right shows the number of each that they sold one day in January.

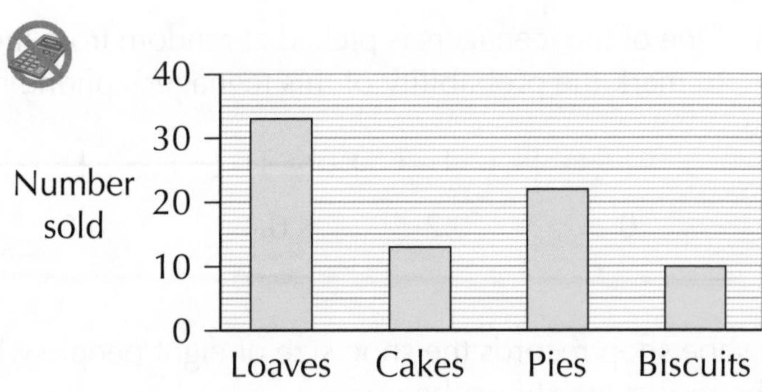

a) How many fewer pies were sold than loaves?

.... 1 mark

b) The store manager says that all the biscuits were bought in packs of 4. Explain how you can tell that the store manager is wrong.

....

....

1 mark

c) The number of cakes sold each day in April is recorded and the range is found to be 12. The greatest number of cakes sold on a day was 52. What was the lowest number of cakes sold on a day?

.... 1 mark

Add up the marks and chart your success...

That's another section in the bag. Nice one. Remember — probability is all about how likely things are, measured from 0 to 1. The closer a probability is to 1, the more likely it is to happen. And as for all those charts, the trick is to read them carefully. All the info you need will be on there somewhere.

Score: $\frac{\quad}{15}$

Answers

Section One — Number

Page 4 — Before you Start

1 7 + 13 = 5 + **15**
12 + 17 = 10 + **19**

2 19 + 32 = **51** (carry 1)
66 − 47 = **19** (6 crossed out to 5, 1 carried)

3 a) 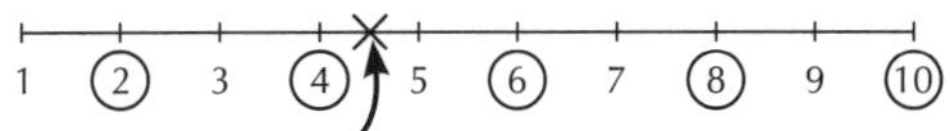 Number line 1 to 10 with 2, 4, 6, 8, 10 circled and a cross marked between 4 and 5.
b) As above

4

×	6	7	8	9
6	36	42	48	54
7	42	49	56	63
8	48	56	64	72
9	54	63	72	81

a) 6 × 9 = 54, so 54 ÷ 6 = **9**
b) 9 × 8 = 72, so 74 ÷ 8 = **9** remainder **2**

5 **4** + **8** = 12 or **8** + **4** = 12
6 − **2** = 4

Page 5 — Place Value and Ordering Numbers

1 **(54)** 105 75 2015 35 7070 25

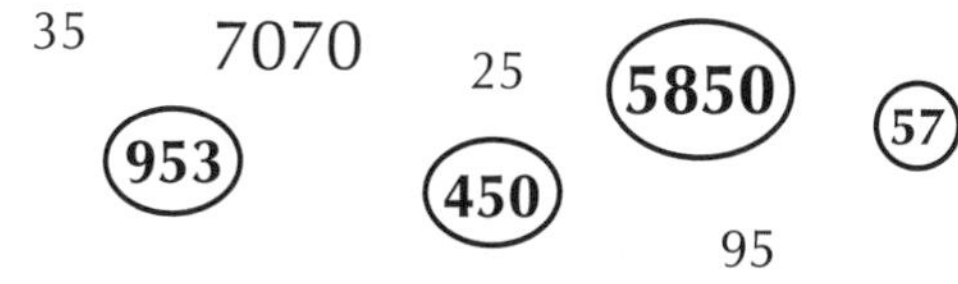

(953) **(450)** **(5850)** **(57)** 95

2 **869 ml**, **896 ml**, **968 ml**, **986 ml**, **989 ml**

3 12 **=** 12 5 **<** 6 7 **>** 4 150 **<** 1500

4 a) **1 098 412** b) **2** c) **8**

Page 6 — Place Value and Ordering Decimals

1 **(0.333)** 0.1 0.25 **(0.03)** **(0.132)** 0.003 0.39 **(0.73)** 0.64 0.3 **(0.131)**

2 1.20 is greater than 1.02, so **Amir** has more yoghurt.

3 **13**, **13.05**, **13.15**, **13.2**, **13.29**, **13.3**

4 □.□□ — 2 digits after and 1 digit before the decimal point.
0.□□ — 0 in the ones column.
0.□5 — 5 in the hundredths column.
0.25 — greater than 0.2 but less than 0.3.

Page 7 — Adding and Subtracting Whole Numbers

1 254 + 347 = **601** (carries 1 1)
156 + 475 = **631** (carries 1 1)
457 − 261 = **196** (4 crossed out to 3, 1 carried)
912 − 335 = **577** (9 crossed out to 8, 1 crossed out to 10, 1 carried)

2 1803 − 796 = **1077** (8 crossed out to 7, 0 crossed out to 16, 1 carried)

3 a) Add the number of pupils in groups M, T and H.
14 + 18 = 32 (carry 1)   32 + 17 = 49
14 + 18 + 17 = **49** pupils.

b) Subtract the number of pupils from the total.
19 + 16 = 35 (carry 1)   35 + 49 = 84 (carry 1)   97 − 84 = 13
97 − 84 = **13** teachers.

Page 8 — Adding and Subtracting Decimals

1 1.5 + 2.3 = **3.8**   4.5 − 3.2 = **1.3**

2 a) 330.0 ml − 20.4 ml = **309.6** ml (3 crossed out to 2, 0 crossed out to 9, 1 carried)

b) 309.6 ml + 43.3 ml = **352.9** ml (carry 1)

3 a) 70p = £0.70
1.30 − 0.70 = 0.60 (1 crossed out to 0, 1 carried)
Sally needs **£0.60**.

b) E.g. 4.50 − 0.60 = 3.90 (4 crossed out to 3, 1 carried)   3.90 − 1.80 = 2.10
Nicky has **£2.10** left over.

4 5.310 + 6.483 = 11.793   11.793 + 8.159 = 19.952 (carries 1 1)
Yes — I can fly. The total is 19.952 kg, which is less than 20 kg.

Page 9 — Multiplying & Dividing by 10, 100, 1000 etc.

1 Lines matching left to right:
5 — 0.05 / 50 / 500 / 5 / 50 000
0.5 — 0.05 / 50 / 500 / 5 / 50 000
0.05
500
0.0005

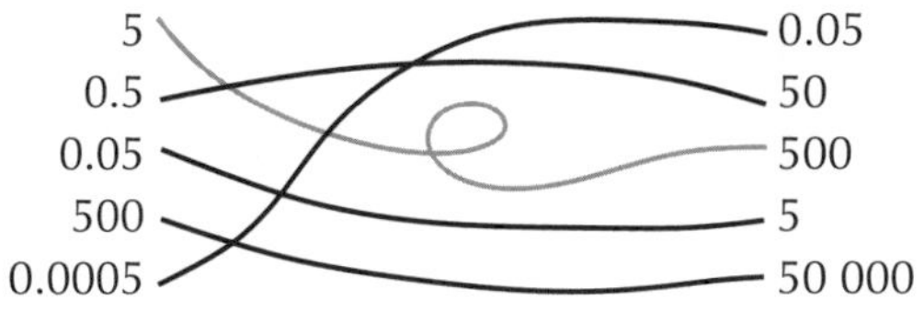

2 1.8 ÷ 10 = **0.18**
0.12 ÷ 100 = **0.0012**
41 500 ÷ 10 000 = **4.15**

3 0.4 [÷] 100 = 0.004
0.0076 [×] 1000 = 7.6
0.3 [÷] 10 = 0.03

4 0.68 × [**100**] = 68
5200 ÷ [**1000**] = 5.2
[**100**] × 0.007 = 0.7

5 1 balloon = 0.012 kg, so
100 balloons = 100 × 0.012 = **1.2 kg**.

Page 10 — Written Multiplication

1

$$\begin{array}{r} 43 \\ \times\ \underline{76} \\ 25_{1}8 \\ +\ \underline{30_{2}10} \\ \underline{\mathbf{3268}} \end{array} \qquad \begin{array}{r} 75 \\ \times\ \underline{98} \\ 60_{4}0 \\ +\ \underline{67_{4}50} \\ \underline{\mathbf{7350}} \\ {\scriptstyle 1\ \ \ \ \ \ } \end{array} \qquad \begin{array}{r} 732 \\ \times\ \underline{54} \\ 29_{1}28 \\ +\ \underline{36_{1}6_{1}00} \\ \underline{\mathbf{39528}} \\ {\scriptstyle 1\ \ \ \ \ \ } \end{array}$$

2 a)

$$\begin{array}{r} 33 \\ \times\ \underline{27} \\ 23_{2}1 \\ +\ \underline{660} \\ \underline{\mathbf{891}} \end{array}$$

b) E.g. 2 + 17 = 19

$$\begin{array}{r} 27 \\ \times\ \underline{19} \\ 24_{6}3 \\ +\ \underline{270} \\ \underline{513} \\ {\scriptstyle 1\ \ \ \ } \end{array} \qquad \begin{array}{r} 891 \\ +\ \underline{513} \\ \underline{1404} \\ {\scriptstyle 1\ \ \ \ } \end{array}$$

So **1404** total passengers.

3 3 × 60 = 180

$$\begin{array}{r} 180 \\ \times\ \underline{52} \\ 3_{1}60 \\ +\ \underline{9_{4}000} \\ \underline{9360} \end{array}$$

So **9360 g** of kale.

Page 11 — Written Division

1 $9\overline{)6^{6}0^{6}3}$ = **67** $\qquad 12\overline{)5^{5}7^{9}6}$ = **48** $\qquad 36\overline{)8^{8}2^{10}8}$ = **23**

2 $6\overline{)3^{3}7^{1}6}$ = 62 r 4

a) **62** egg cartons

b) **4** eggs left over

3 $13\overline{)7^{7}6^{11}7}$ = 59

So one ticket costs **£59**.

4 $8\overline{)2^{2}7^{3}0}$ = 33 r 6

So 270 ÷ 8 = **33** remainder **6**.

$$\begin{array}{r} 22 \\ 18\overline{)^{3}\cancel{4}^{1}10} \\ -\ \underline{36}\downarrow \\ ^{4}\cancel{5}^{1}0 \\ -\ \underline{36} \\ \underline{14} \end{array}$$

So 410 ÷ 18 = **22** remainder **14**.

5

$$\begin{array}{r} 96 \\ 52\overline{)4992} \\ -\ \underline{468}\downarrow \\ 312 \\ -\ \underline{312} \\ \underline{0} \end{array}$$

So **96 packs** of cards.

Page 12 — Negative Numbers

1 Number line: –10, **–9**, **–6**, –5, **–2**, 0

2 **–11, –6, –4, 2, 4, 10**

3 6 + –2 = **4** $\qquad$ –3 – 7 = **–10**

–1 – –5 = **4** $\qquad$ –4 + –7 = **–11**

4 –2 < –5 ☒ $\qquad$ –4 ≥ –6 ☑ $\qquad$ –7 ≤ –10 ☒ $\qquad$ –8 > –3 ☒

5 a) Edward's score is –6 + –4 + 9 = –1.
This is not 10, so Edward **did not win**.

b) **Yes** — by throwing the dart scoring –4 again and hitting 7. The new score would be –6 + 7 + 9 = 10, so he would win.

Page 13 — BODMAS

1 a) 6 + 8 ÷ 4 – 2 = 6 + 2 – 2 = 8 – 2 = **6**

b) 2 × 3 – 9 ÷ 3 = 2 × 3 – 3 = 6 – 3 = **3**

2 **(4 + 5) × 2 – 3**

3 a) (1 + 3) × 2 = 8 $\qquad$ b) 8 – (2 + 1) = 5

c) 12 ÷ (3 + 1) = 3 $\qquad$ d) (4 + 2) × (3 + 1) = 24

4 a) **3 + 3**

b) E.g. **3 – (3 + 3)**

c) E.g. **3 × 3 – (3 + 3)**

Page 14 — Inverse Operations

1 39 [–] 15 = 24

2 **60 ÷ 4**

You could also answer 60 ÷ 15.

3

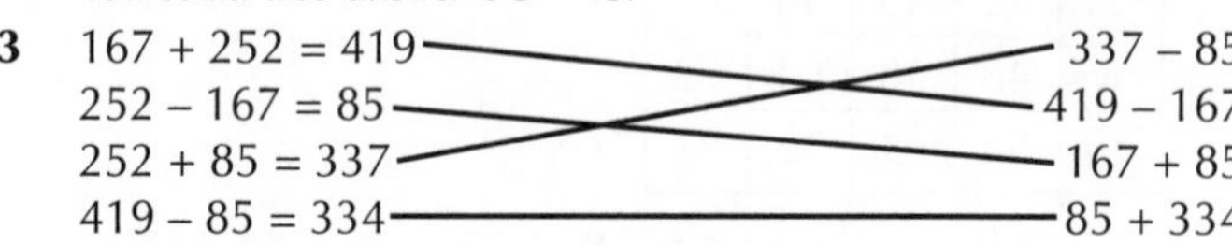

167 + 252 = 419 — 419 – 167
252 – 167 = 85 — 167 + 85
252 + 85 = 337 — 337 – 85
419 – 85 = 334 — 85 + 334

4 **1795**

× 1034 is inverse to ÷ 1034, so they cancel out.

5 a) E.g. **25 × 4 = 100**, not 125.

b) E.g. **140 ÷ 7 = 20**, not 18.

Page 15 — Rounding

1 **10** protractors $\qquad$ **30** rulers

170 staples $\qquad$ **130** inflatable globes

2 5.4 rounds to **5**

3.8 rounds to **4**

14.3 rounds to **14**

3 **149 cm**

4 145 = 100 to the nearest **100**

12 479 = 12 000 to the nearest **1000**

129 = 130 to the nearest **10**

40 009 = 40 010 to the nearest **10**

5 a) **Yes** — 27 = 30 to the nearest ten.

b) **25 apples**. 25 = 30 to the nearest ten, but 24 = 20 to the nearest ten.

Page 16 — Estimating

1 40 + 10 + 20 + 10 = **80**

2 **24 – 12 = 12** $\qquad$ **10 – 15 = –5**

3 **30 × 20 = 600** $\qquad$ **100 × 150 = 15 000**

4 44 000 ÷ 200 = 440 ÷ 2 = 220.
So there are approximately **220 words per page**.

5 a) 1000 × 400 = **400 000**

b) **Yes** — Jason's answer is over 10 times the estimate.

Page 17 — Powers and Roots

1 a) [3 by 3 grid of squares]

b) 3^2 = **3 × 3 = 9**

c) E.g. The large square is made up of 9 smaller squares in a 3 by 3 grid.

2 a) b)

<u>4</u>	(27)	32	<u>25</u>	(8)
6	<u>36</u>	18	<u>16</u>	3
5	52	(64)	<u>49</u>	7

64 is both 8^2 and 4^3 — sneaky.

3 $\sqrt{64}$ = **8 m**

4 $\sqrt[3]{8}$ = **2** $\sqrt{81}$ = **9** 5^3 = **125** $\sqrt[3]{216}$ = **6**

Page 18 — Multiples and LCM

1 **C** is correct — they are all multiples of 5.

2 a) 1 2 (3) 4 5 (6) 7 8 (9) 10 11 (12) 13 14 (15) 16 17 (18)

b) 1 2 3 (4) 5 6 7 (8) 9 10 11 (12) 13 14 15 (16) 17 18

c) **12** *It's the smallest number circled on all three lines.*

3 a) Multiples of 6 are: 6, 12, 18, 24, ...
Multiples of 8 are: 8, 16, 24, ...
So the lowest common multiple is 24, i.e. they will first cross the line together after **24 minutes**.

b) 2 hours = 120 minutes and 120 = 24 × 5.
So 120 is the LCM of 6, 8 and 5.
So the shortest possible time is **5 minutes**.

Page 19 — Factors and HCF

1 a) **1**, **2**, **3**, **6**, **9** and **18** b) **1** and **3**

2 a) **1**, **2**, **5** and **10**

b) (i) **10**

(ii) Divide each quantity by 10.
1 chocolate bar, **3** lollipops and **7** gummy bears

3 a) (i) **1, 2, 3, 4, 5, 6, 10, 12, 15, 20, 30, 60**

(ii) **1, 2, 3, 4, 6, 7, 12, 14, 21, 28, 42, 84**

b) Factors of 140: 1, 2, 4, 5, 7, 10, 14, 20, 28, 35, 70, 140.
So the highest common factor is **4**.

Page 20 — Prime Numbers

1

2 49 = 7 × 7, so 49 has more factors than itself and 1.

3 a)

~~2~~	~~3~~	~~4~~	~~5~~	~~6~~
7	~~8~~	~~9~~	~~10~~	11
~~12~~	13	~~14~~	~~15~~	~~16~~
17	~~18~~	19	~~20~~	~~21~~

b) **7**, **11**, **13**, **17** and **19**

c) (i) **Yes** — they are **not divisible** by any number other than **1** and **themselves**.

(ii) **No** — 2, 3 and 5 are **also primes**.

4 ☑ 2 is the only even prime number.
True — all other even numbers are divisible by 2.

☐ All numbers ending in 3 are prime.
False — e.g. 33 is not prime (33 = 3 × 11).

☑ There is only one prime number ending in 5.
True — since 5 is a prime number and any other number ending in 5 is divisible by 5.

☐ There are no prime numbers greater than 100.
False — for example, 101 is prime.

Pages 21-22 — Review Exercise

1 a) (i) **4** ***[1 mark]*** (ii) The **hundreds** column. ***[1 mark]***

b) (i) **1.4503** ***[1 mark]*** (ii) **4** ***[1 mark]***

c) **14 500** ***[1 mark]***

2 a)
```
   2189
 +  847
   3036   [1 mark]
   111
```

b)
```
   624.10
 −  33.59
   590.51   [1 mark]
```

c)
```
      5435
  ×     63
     16305
 + 326100
    342405   [1 mark]
```

d)
```
        43   [1 mark]
 51 | 2193
     −204↓
       153
      −153
         0
```

3 1 − 3 = **−2 °C** ***[1 mark]***

4 7 − 10 ÷ 2 + (−4 + 2) = 7 − 5 + (−2)
= 2 + −2
= **0** ***[1 mark]***

5 a) 20 × 90 = **1800** ***[1 mark]***

b) **1653 ÷ 19** or **1653 ÷ 87** ***[1 mark]***

6 a) $2^3 = 2 \times 2 \times 2 = 8$ and $3^2 = 3 \times 3 = 9$, so $\mathbf{3^2}$ is bigger ***[1 mark]***.

b) $\sqrt{3^2 + 4^2} = \sqrt{9 + 16} = \sqrt{25} = \mathbf{5}$ ***[1 mark]***

7 The lowest common multiple of 2, 3 and 4 is 12.
So the lowest common multiple of 20 cm, 30 cm and 40 cm is 120 cm.
So the smallest possible height is **120 cm** ***[1 mark]***.

8 a) **1**, **2** and **4** ***[1 mark]***

b) **4 snack boxes** ***[1 mark]***. It's the highest common factor of 12, 20 and 28 ***[1 mark]***.
[2 marks available in total — as above]

9

3 13 11 17 17 29 21 63 27 41 19 53

[2 marks available — 2 marks for the path shown, otherwise 1 mark for a path with only one non-prime included]

Section Two — Proportions and Units

Page 23 — Before you Start

1 E.g.

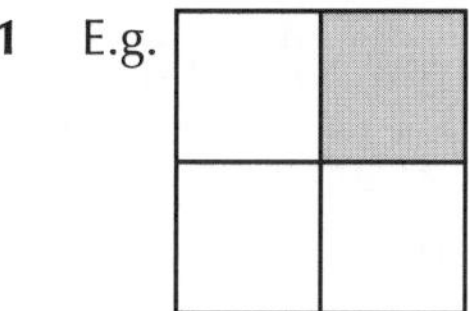

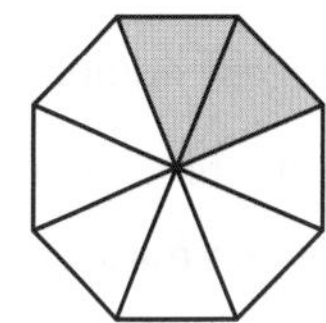

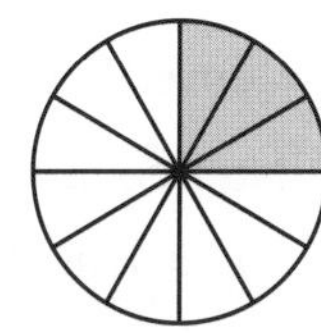

You can shade whichever sections you want, just so long as you've shaded the correct number of sections for each shape.

2  $\frac{4}{16}$ $\frac{7}{12}$ $\boxed{\frac{3}{15}}$ $\frac{8}{20}$ $\boxed{\frac{10}{50}}$

3 $\frac{1}{4}$ = **25%** $\frac{7}{10}$ = **70%** $\frac{3}{6} = \frac{1}{2}$ = **50%**

4 $\mathbf{\frac{3}{7}}$ $\mathbf{\frac{1}{2}}$ $\mathbf{\frac{5}{6}}$

5 a) The arrow points exactly halfway between the 40 and 50 mph markers, so the scale shows **45 mph**.
b) There are ten small divisions between 100 and 200, so each one is worth 10 ml. The line is six marks up from 100, so it shows 100 + (6 × 10) = **160 ml**.
c) There are five small divisions between 20 and 30, so each one is worth 2 °C. The line is two marks up from 20, so it shows 20 + (2 × 2) = **24 °C**.

Page 24 — Equivalent Fractions

1 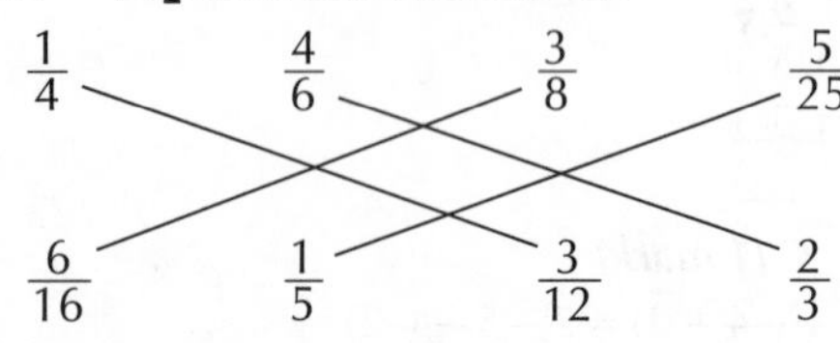

$\frac{1}{4}$ $\frac{4}{6}$ $\frac{3}{8}$ $\frac{5}{25}$

$\frac{6}{16}$ $\frac{1}{5}$ $\frac{3}{12}$ $\frac{2}{3}$

2 a) $\frac{2}{5} = \frac{16}{40}$ and $\frac{3}{8} = \frac{15}{40}$.
$\frac{2}{5}$ is bigger, so more people said **speed knitting**.
b) $\frac{6}{40} = \mathbf{\frac{3}{20}}$

3 5, 12 and 15 are all factors of 60, so use 60 as the common denominator.
Julia ate $\frac{2}{5} = \frac{2\times12}{5\times12} = \frac{24}{60}$, so has $\frac{36}{60}$ of her sweets left.
Parvinder ate $\frac{5}{12} = \frac{5\times5}{12\times5} = \frac{25}{60}$, so has $\frac{35}{60}$ left.
Richard ate $\frac{7}{15} = \frac{7\times4}{15\times4} = \frac{28}{60}$, so has $\frac{32}{60}$ left.
So the order is **Richard**, **Parvinder**, **Julia**.

Page 25 — Mixed Numbers and Improper Fractions

1 $1\frac{2}{3} = \frac{3}{3} + \frac{2}{3} = \frac{5}{3}$, so $1\frac{2}{3} > \frac{4}{3}$.

2

Mixed Number	Improper Fraction
$3\frac{1}{2}$	$\mathbf{\frac{7}{2}}$
$\mathbf{1\frac{3}{5}}$	$\frac{8}{5}$
$\mathbf{2\frac{4}{7}}$	$\frac{18}{7}$
$7\frac{2}{3}$	$\mathbf{\frac{23}{3}}$

3 $\frac{3}{4}$ is the only fraction less than 1, so that is the smallest.
Convert $\frac{8}{3}$ to a mixed number: $\frac{8}{3} = \frac{6}{3} + \frac{2}{3} = 2\frac{2}{3}$.
Now compare $2\frac{2}{3}$ and $2\frac{3}{8}$: $\frac{2}{3} > \frac{1}{2}$ and $\frac{3}{8} < \frac{1}{2}$,
so $\frac{3}{8} < \frac{2}{3}$ and therefore $2\frac{2}{3} = \frac{8}{3}$ is bigger.
$3\frac{2}{7}$ is bigger than 3, so the order is $\mathbf{\frac{3}{4}}$, $\mathbf{2\frac{3}{8}}$, $\mathbf{\frac{8}{3}}$, $\mathbf{3\frac{2}{7}}$.

4 Convert $\frac{13}{9}$ to a mixed number: $\frac{13}{9} = \frac{9}{9} + \frac{4}{9} = 1\frac{4}{9}$.
Now compare the fractional parts: $\frac{2}{5} = \frac{18}{45}$ and $\frac{4}{9} = \frac{20}{45}$.
So the longer pet is **Jemma's** grasshopper.

Pages 26-27 — Adding and Subtracting Fractions

1 a) E.g. 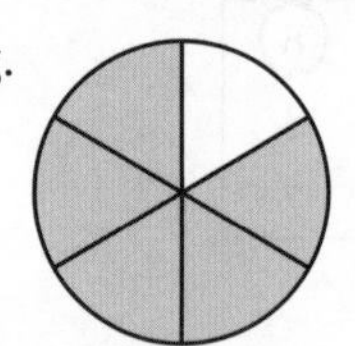 b) $\mathbf{\frac{1}{6}}$

You can shade any five of the six slices.

2 $\frac{1}{4} + \frac{2}{4} = \frac{1+2}{4} = \mathbf{\frac{3}{4}}$
$\frac{4}{3} - \frac{2}{3} = \frac{4-2}{3} = \mathbf{\frac{2}{3}}$
$1\frac{2}{7} + 2\frac{3}{7} = 1 + 2 + \frac{2}{7} + \frac{3}{7} = 3 + \frac{5}{7} = \mathbf{3\frac{5}{7}}$
$3\frac{3}{7} - 1\frac{6}{7} = \frac{24}{7} - \frac{13}{7} = \frac{24-13}{7} = \frac{11}{7} = \mathbf{1\frac{4}{7}}$

3 $1 - \frac{5}{19} - \frac{3}{19} = \mathbf{\frac{11}{19}}$

4 $10\frac{7}{8} - 2\frac{3}{8} = (10 - 2) + (\frac{7}{8} - \frac{3}{8}) = 8 + \frac{4}{8} = \mathbf{8\frac{1}{2}}$ **miles**

5 Use 10 as the common denominator: $\frac{3}{5} = \frac{6}{10}$
So the fraction that are spinach flavour is $1 - \frac{1}{10} - \frac{6}{10} = \mathbf{\frac{3}{10}}$.

6 $\frac{1}{2} + \frac{3}{4} = \frac{2}{4} + \frac{3}{4} = \frac{5}{4} = \mathbf{1\frac{1}{4}}$
$\frac{15}{9} - 1\frac{5}{18} = 1\frac{6}{9} - 1\frac{5}{18} = 1\frac{12}{18} - 1\frac{5}{18} = \mathbf{\frac{7}{18}}$
$2\frac{4}{9} + 6\frac{2}{3} = 2\frac{4}{9} + 6\frac{6}{9} = 8 + \frac{10}{9} = \mathbf{9\frac{1}{9}}$

7 a) $1\frac{1}{2} + \frac{7}{4} + 1\frac{3}{8} = 1\frac{4}{8} + 1\frac{6}{8} + 1\frac{3}{8}$
$= 3 + \frac{13}{8} = 3 + 1\frac{5}{8} = \mathbf{4\frac{5}{8}}$ **baskets**
b) Lei picked $\frac{7}{4} - 1\frac{3}{8} = 1\frac{6}{8} - 1\frac{3}{8} = \frac{3}{8}$ of a basket more than Quentin. One basket holds approximately 80 blackberries, so Lei picked approximately $80 \times \frac{3}{8} = 80 \div 8 \times 3 =$ **30 blackberries** more.
You could also estimate how many each person picked and then subtract them.

Page 28 — Multiplying Fractions by Whole Numbers

1 $\frac{1}{2} \times 32 = 32 \div 2 = \mathbf{16}$ $\frac{1}{6} \times 48 = 48 \div 6 = \mathbf{8}$
$\frac{3}{10} \times 100 = (100 \div 10) \times 3 = 10 \times 3 = \mathbf{30}$

2 a) $120 \times \frac{1}{10} = 120 \div 10 = \mathbf{12}$
b) $1 - \frac{1}{10} - \frac{2}{5} = 1 - \frac{1}{10} - \frac{4}{10} = \frac{5}{10} = \frac{1}{2}$ of the marbles are purple. So $120 \times \frac{1}{2} = 120 \div 2 =$ **60** are purple.
You could also do $120 \times \frac{5}{10}$ but it's easier if you simplify the fraction.

3 $\frac{1}{2} \times 15 = \frac{15}{2} = \mathbf{7\frac{1}{2}}$
$\frac{2}{3} \times 11 = \frac{22}{3} = \mathbf{7\frac{1}{3}}$
$\frac{3}{4} \times 22 = \frac{66}{4} = \mathbf{16\frac{1}{2}}$

4 a) $450 \times \frac{2}{9} = 450 \div 9 \times 2 = 50 \times 2 =$ **100 blue bananas**
b) The robot makes $450 \times \frac{1}{15} = 450 \div 15 = 30$ blue bananas after its parts are replaced, so each day it makes 100 – 30 = **70 fewer blue bananas**.

Pages 29-30 — Fractions, Decimals and Percentages

1 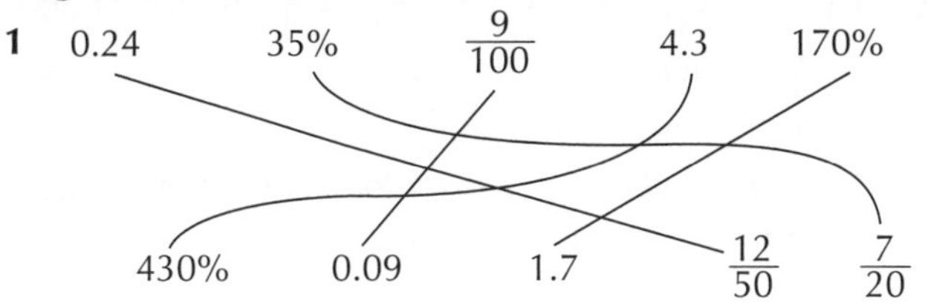

2 a) $32\% = 32 \div 100 = \mathbf{0.32}$ b) $\frac{7}{25} = \frac{28}{100} = \mathbf{28\%}$

c) $0.54 = \frac{54}{100} = \mathbf{\frac{27}{50}}$

3 $\frac{9}{20} = \frac{45}{100} = 0.45$ and $0.45 \times 100 = 45\%$

$80\% = \frac{80}{100} = \frac{4}{5}$ and $\frac{80}{100} = 0.8$

$0.24 = \frac{24}{100} = \frac{6}{25}$ and $0.24 \times 100 = 24\%$

So the completed table is:

Fraction	Decimal	Percentage
$\frac{9}{20}$	**0.45**	**45%**
$\mathbf{\frac{4}{5}}$	**0.8**	80%
$\mathbf{\frac{6}{25}}$	0.24	**24%**

4 a) $\frac{3}{20} = \frac{15}{100} = \mathbf{15\%}$

b) $40\% - 15\% = 25\% = \mathbf{\frac{1}{4}}$ of the teams

5 $\frac{36}{40} = \frac{9}{10} = 90\%$, so George scored a higher proportion of the marks in **maths**.

6 a) $\frac{2}{5} = \frac{4}{10} = 40\%$, so Cathy is **incorrect**.

b) $\frac{1}{4} + \frac{3}{10} + \frac{2}{5} = 25\% + 30\% + 40\% = 95\%$ of the plants are cucumbers, tomatoes or chillies, so **5%** aren't.

7 a) $\frac{14}{25} = \frac{56}{100} = \mathbf{0.56}$

b) Before, he had seen 0.56 = 56% of the films.
Now that he's watched another 24%, he's watched a total of $56\% + 24\% = 80\% = \frac{80}{100} = \mathbf{\frac{4}{5}}$ of the films.

Page 31 — Finding Percentages Without a Calculator

1 35% of 100 = **35** 10% of 170 = 170 ÷ 10 = **17**
20% of 200 = 200 ÷ 5 = **40**

2 a) 10% of 80 = 80 ÷ 10 = 8, so 30% of 80 = 3 × 8 = **24**

b) 30% + 10% = 40%, so 100% – 40% = 60% of the patterns are for neither scarves nor hats.
50% of 80 = 80 ÷ 2 = 40 and 10% of 80 = 8,
so 60% of 80 = 40 + 8 = **48**.
Split up hard percentages into percentages that are easier to find, then add all the results together.

3 a) 10% of 150 = 150 ÷ 10 = 15
2% of 150 = 15 ÷ 5 = 3
So 12% of 150 = 15 + 3 = 18
So she keeps 150 – 18 = **132 stickers**.

b) 60% of 150 = 15 × 6 = 90
So she keeps 90 – 7 = **83 Rollerham Rovers stickers**.

Page 32 — Finding Percentages Using a Calculator

1 18% of 250 = 0.18 × 250 = **45**
4% of 675 = 0.04 × 675 = **27**
162% of 1050 = 1.62 × 1050 = **1701**

2 a) 57% of £26 = 0.57 × 26 = **£14.82**

b) In total, he spends 11% + 57% = 68% of his money, so he has 32% left. 32% of 26 = 0.32 × 26 = **£8.32**

3 a) 23% of 860 = 0.23 × 860 = **197.8 g**

b) 12% of £37 = 0.12 × 37 = £4.44. This is more than £4, so Pauline should choose the ☑ **12% discount**.

Pages 33-34 — Ratios and Comparing

1 There are 2 sea lions and 5 balls, so the ratio of sea lions to balls is **2:5**.

2 15 as a fraction of 25 = $\frac{15}{25} = \mathbf{\frac{3}{5}}$

60 as a fraction of 42 = $\frac{60}{42} = \mathbf{\frac{10}{7}}$

12 as a percentage of 48 = $\frac{12}{48} \times 100 = \frac{1}{4} \times 100 = \mathbf{25\%}$

30 as a percentage of 20 = $\frac{30}{20} \times 100 = \frac{3}{2} \times 100 = \mathbf{150\%}$

3 a) There are 6 pizza slices and 3 carrots, so the ratio of pizza slices to carrots is **6:3**.

b) Both sides of the ratio can be divided by 3, so the ratio in its simplest form is **2:1**.

4 10% of 70 = 7 and 20% of 25 = 5, so 10% of 70 **>** 20% of 25.
$\frac{3}{4}$ of 40 = 30 and $\frac{3}{2}$ of 20 = 30, so $\frac{3}{4}$ of 40 **=** $\frac{3}{2}$ of 20.
$\frac{2}{3}$ of 21 = 14 and $\frac{3}{8}$ of 32 = 12, so $\frac{2}{3}$ of 21 **>** $\frac{3}{8}$ of 32.
10% of 60 = 6 and 5% of 60 = 3, so 15% of 60 = 9.
25% of 40 = 10, so 15% of 60 **<** 25% of 40.

5 The ratio of plates to mugs is 5 : 3, and there are 10 = 5 × 2 plates. So there must be 3 × 2 = **6 mugs**.

6 a) 1.95 as a fraction of 2.6 = $\frac{1.95}{2.6} = \mathbf{\frac{3}{4}}$

b) There is 2.6 – 1.95 = 0.65 m^2 of fabric left over.
0.52 as a percentage of 0.65 = $\frac{0.52}{0.65} \times 100 = \mathbf{80\%}$

7 a) $\frac{240}{600} = \frac{24}{60} = \frac{24 \div 12}{60 \div 12} = \mathbf{\frac{2}{5}}$

b) $\frac{330}{1000} = \frac{33}{100} = 33\%$ and $\frac{2}{5} = 40\%$.
So **William** has drunk more.

Pages 35-36 — Time

1 22:22 is 10:22 pm and so is later than 10:10 pm.
So **Alexis** goes to bed at the later time.

2 12-hour: **5:15 pm** 12-hour: **6:30 pm** 12-hour: **4:40 pm**
24-hour: **17:15** 24-hour: **18:30** 24-hour: **16:40**

3 a) 15:49 + 22 minutes = 16:00 + 11 minutes = **16:11**

b) 08:30 – 48 minutes = 08:00 – 18 minutes = **7:42 am**

4 a) 60 minutes = 1 hour
So 180 minutes = 180 ÷ 60 = **3 hours**.

b) 1 hour = 60 minutes
2 hours = 60 × 2 = 120 minutes
0.5 hours = 60 ÷ 2 = 30 minutes
So 2.5 hours = 120 + 30 = **150 minutes**.

c) 1 minute = 60 seconds
5 minutes = 60 × 5 = 300 seconds
$\frac{1}{4}$ of a minute = 60 ÷ 4 = 15 seconds
So $5\frac{1}{4}$ minutes = 300 + 15 = **315 seconds**.

5 a) The last bus that gets to Redmile Road before 08:00 leaves Neptune Street at **07:33**.

b) E.g. 07:32 – 07:08 = **24 minutes**

c) The 07:56 bus should leave Redmile Road at 07:41.
07:52 – 07:41 = 11 minutes, so it's running 11 minutes late. 07:56 + 11 minutes = **08:07**

6 a) **3:25 pm**

b) There are 45 minutes from 16:15 to 17:00, and then 55 minutes from 17:00 to 17:55. So Sandcastle Building starts 45 + 55 = **100 minutes** later than Sock Puppet Shakespeare.

c) 17:55 + 85 minutes = 18:00 + 80 minutes = 19:00 + 20 minutes = **19:20**

Pages 37-38 — Units and Measuring

1

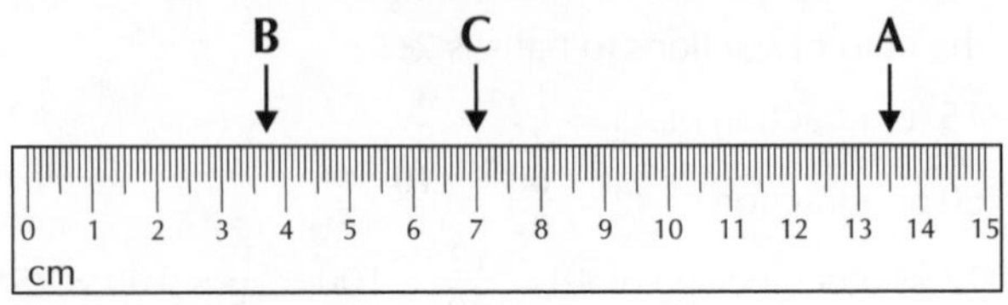

For part b), 37 mm = 37 ÷ 10 = 3.7 cm.
For part c), 0.07 m = 0.07 × 100 = 7 cm.

2 550 cm = 550 ÷ 100 = **5.5 m**
550 cm = 550 × 10 = **5500 mm**

3 24 mm = 2.4 cm, 0.2 m = 20 cm, 2.3 mm = 0.23 cm
So the order is: **2.3 mm, 2.3 cm, 24 mm, 0.2 m, 21 cm**

4 4.23 litres = 4.23 × 1000 = **4230 ml**
76 g = 76 ÷ 1000 = **0.076 kg**

5 287 mm = 287 ÷ 10 = 28.7 cm
Then 28.7 cm = 28.7 ÷ 100 = **0.287 m**

6 750 m = 0.75 km and 5000 m = 5 km, so the total length is 0.75 + 19.4 + 5 = **25.15 km**

7 a) 525 g = 0.525 kg and 175 g = 0.175 kg, so the total mass is 0.525 + 0.175 + 0.35 = **1.05 kg**

b) 1.05 kg = 1.05 × 1000 = 1050 g.
She can make 1050 ÷ 30 = 35 biscuits.
Yes — the recipe makes enough.
Alternatively, 32 biscuits require 30 × 32 = 960 g = 0.96 kg of ingredients, which is less than 1.05 kg.

8 a) 750 ml = 0.75 litres and 320 ml = 0.32 litres, so the total volume of fruit punch is 0.75 + 0.45 + 0.32 + 1.3 = **2.82 litres**

b) 2.82 litres = 2.82 × 1000 = 2820 ml. He can pour 2820 ÷ 180 = $15\frac{2}{3}$ glasses, so **15 whole glasses**.

c) There is $\frac{2}{3}$ of a glass left over, so $\frac{2}{3}$ × 180 = **120 ml**.

Pages 39-40 — Review Exercise

1 a) $\frac{6}{18} = \frac{6 \div 6}{18 \div 6} = \mathbf{\frac{1}{3}}$ ***[1 mark]***

b) $\frac{8}{28} = \frac{8 \div 4}{28 \div 4} = \mathbf{\frac{2}{7}}$ ***[1 mark]***

c) $\frac{45}{36} = \frac{45 \div 9}{36 \div 9} = \mathbf{\frac{5}{4}}$ ***[1 mark]***

2 $\frac{7}{12}$ is the only fraction less than 1, so this is the smallest.
$\frac{9}{4} = 2\frac{1}{4}$, $\frac{11}{5} = 2\frac{1}{5}$ and $\frac{1}{9} < \frac{1}{5} < \frac{1}{4}$, so $2\frac{1}{9} < \frac{11}{5} < \frac{9}{4}$.
$1\frac{2}{3}$ is bigger than 1 and less than 2.
So the order is $\mathbf{\frac{7}{12}, 1\frac{2}{3}, 2\frac{1}{9}, \frac{11}{5}, \frac{9}{4}}$.
[2 marks available — 2 marks for all five in the correct order, otherwise 1 mark for no more than one out of order]

3 a) $\frac{5}{9} + \frac{1}{3} = \frac{5}{9} + \frac{3}{9} = \mathbf{\frac{8}{9}}$ ***[1 mark]***

b) $2\frac{3}{10} - \frac{2}{5} = \frac{23}{10} - \frac{4}{10} = \frac{19}{10} = \mathbf{1\frac{9}{10}}$ ***[1 mark]***

4 a) $\frac{7}{20} = \frac{35}{100}$ = **35%** ***[1 mark]***

b) 60 × $\frac{2}{5}$ = (60 ÷ 5) × 2 = 12 × 2 = **24 songs** ***[1 mark]***

c) E.g. $\frac{2}{5} + \frac{7}{20} = \frac{8}{20} + \frac{7}{20} = \frac{15}{20} = \frac{3}{4}$ are rock or jazz, so $\frac{1}{4}$ are neither rock nor jazz.
$\frac{1}{4}$ of 60 = 60 ÷ 4 = **15 songs**
[2 marks available — 1 mark for a correct method, 1 mark for a correct answer]
Alternatively, you could work out $\frac{7}{20}$ of 60 and subtract this and 24 from 60.

5 10% of 40 = 4, so 30% of 40 = 3 × 4 = **12 cats**. ***[1 mark]***

6 a) 15 as a fraction of 45 = $\frac{15}{45} = \mathbf{\frac{1}{3}}$ ***[1 mark]***

b) 21 as a percentage of 7 = $\frac{21}{7}$ × 100 = 3 × 100 = **300%** ***[1 mark]***

7 There are 7 needles and 3 haystacks, so the ratio of needles to haystacks is **7 : 3**. ***[1 mark]***

8 The train should have arrived 14 minutes earlier than 14:09, so it should have arrived at 13:55.
Then find the time from 11:47 to 13:55:
11:47 → 13:47 = 2 hours
13:47 → 13:55 = 8 minutes
So **2 hours 8 minutes**.
[2 marks available — 1 mark for a correct method, 1 mark for the correct answer]

9 0.125 kg = 125 g, 0.45 kg = 450 g and 1.2 kg = 1200 g ***[1 mark]***. Yan already has 125 + 450 + 385 = 960 g of jam, so she still needs 1200 – 960 = **240 g** ***[1 mark]***.
[2 marks available in total — as above]

Section Three — Algebra and Graphs

Page 41 — Before you Start

1 **58**

2 b) 5, 10, 15, 20, **25**, **30**, **35** **Add 5**

c) 31, 27, 23, 19, **15**, **11**, **7** **Subtract 4**

3 P = 5 + 2 + 5 + 2 = **14 cm**
Don't forget to write the units if they're not given.

4 $\mathbf{x = 1, y = 2}$ or $\mathbf{x = 3, y = 1}$

5 a) **A = (3, 6), B = (2, 3), C = (6, 2)**

b)

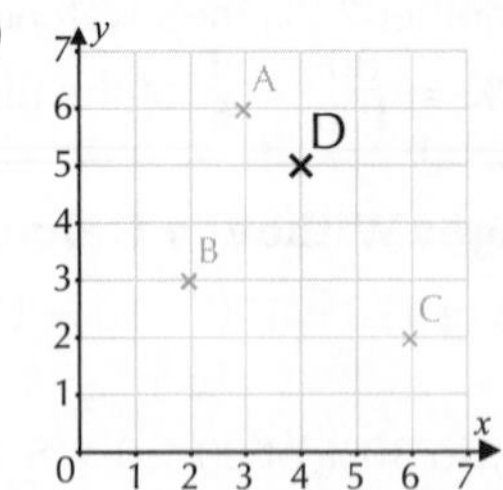

Page 42 — Simplifying Expressions

1 Collect the x's: $6x - 3x + x = 4x$
Collect the y's: $5y + 2y = 7y$
Collect the z's: $2z + z = 3z$
Collect the numbers: 12 – 7 = 5
So the simplified expression = $\mathbf{4x + 7y + 3z + 5}$
You could write the terms in any order.

2 a) $\mathbf{2x + y}$ b) $\mathbf{7y - 2x + 7}$ c) $\mathbf{2x + y}$
So the expression that's the odd one out is **b)**.

3

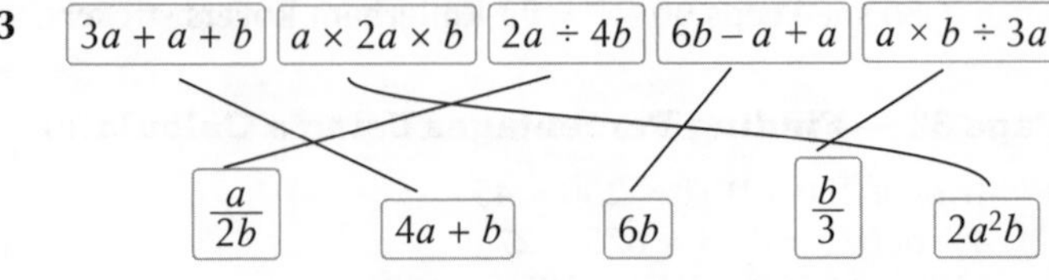

4 a) Jacket price = $x - 15$, shirt price = $\frac{1}{2}y$
Cost of one jacket and four shirts = $\mathbf{(x - 15) + (4 \times \frac{1}{2}y)}$
b) $\mathbf{x + 2y - 15}$

Pages 43-44 — Solving Equations

1 a) $a = 60 - 10 = \mathbf{50}$
b) $b = 31 - 19 = \mathbf{12}$
c) $c = 20 + 16 = \mathbf{36}$
d) $d = 4 - 8 = \mathbf{-4}$

2 $a = 12 \div 4 = 3$
$b = 25 \div 5 = 5$
$c = 4 \times 2 = 8$
$d = 3 \times 3 = 9$

a — 3
b — 5
c — 8
d — 9

3 a) $2a = 13 - 3$
$2a = 10$
$a = 10 \div 2$
$a = \mathbf{5}$
b) $8b = 21 + 3$
$8b = 24$
$b = 24 \div 8$
$b = \mathbf{3}$
c) $10c = 72 - 12$
$10c = 60$
$c = 60 \div 10$
$c = \mathbf{6}$
d) $50d = 250 + 100$
$50d = 350$
$d = 350 \div 50$
$d = \mathbf{7}$

4 $3x + 2 = 11$, $3x = 9$, $x = 3$
$7x = 21$, $x = 21 \div 7$, $x = 3$
$5x + 3 = 18$, $5x = 15$, $x = 3$

Circled: $3x + 2 = 11$, $7x = 21$, $5x + 3 = 18$
Not circled: $89 - x = 92$, $18x = 36$, $3x - 2 = 2$

5 a) $7x = 12$ ☒
$x = 12 \div 7 = 1.714...$
b) $3x - 3 = 3$ ☑
$3x = 3 + 3 = 6$
$x = 6 \div 3 = 2$
c) $5 - x = 4$ ☒
$x = 5 - 4 = 1$
d) $8x + 9 = 25$ ☑
$8x = 25 - 9 = 16$
$x = 16 \div 8 = 2$

6 a) Hannah ate n pieces, Greg ate $4n$ and there were 7 left over so in total there were $4n + n + 7$ pieces, so the correct equation is $\mathbf{5n + 7 = 62}$
b) $5n = 62 - 7$
$5n = 55$
$n = 55 \div 5$
$n = \mathbf{11}$

7 $3x - 2 = 4$ — $7x - 10 = 2x$
$4x = 4$ — $3x - 5 = -2x$
$4x - 3 = 9$ — $2x - 5 = 1$

8 a) $17x + 31 = 510 + 31 = \mathbf{541}$
b) $170x = 10 \times 17x = 10 \times 510 = \mathbf{5100}$
c) $1700x - 500 = 100 \times 17x - 500$
$= 100 \times 510 - 500$
$= 51\,000 - 500$
$= \mathbf{50\,500}$

9 $4x - 9 = 2x + 3$
$4x = 2x + 12$
$2x = 12$
$\mathbf{x = 6}$

Page 45 — Substituting into Expressions and Formulas

1 a) $(5 \times 6) - 3 = 30 - 3 = \mathbf{27}$
b) $(10 \times 2) + (7 \times 4) = 20 + 28 = \mathbf{48}$
c) $100 + (3 \times 5) - (8 \times 3) = 100 + 15 - 24 = \mathbf{91}$

2 $3t + 7$: $(3 \times 4) + 7 = 12 + 7 = 19$
$33 - 6t$: $33 - (6 \times 4) = 33 - 24 = 9$
$\frac{10t}{2}$: $(10 \times 4) \div 2 = 40 \div 2 = 20$
$50t - 189$: $(50 \times 4) - 189 = 200 - 189 = 11$
So, in order, the equations are:
$\mathbf{33 - 6t}$ $\mathbf{50t - 189}$ $\mathbf{3t + 7}$ $\mathbf{\frac{10t}{2}}$

3 $s = 27 \div 3 = \mathbf{9}$

4 a) $T = 35 + (50 \times 0.5) = 35 + 25 =$ **60 minutes**
b) $50 = 35 + 50w$
$15 = 50w$
$w = 15 \div 50 =$ **0.3 kg**

Pages 46-47 — Sequences

1 2, 5, 8, 11... — Add 3
67, 56, 45, 34.... — Subtract 11
3, 6 ,12, 24... — Multiply by 2
−3, 1, 5, 9... — Add 4
16, 8, 4, 2... — Divide by 2
2, −5, −12, −19... — Subtract 7

2 a) −3, 6, **15**, 24, 33
The rule is add 9 each time.
b) **7**, 12, 17, **22** 27
The rule is add 5 each time.
c) −2, **−10**, −18, −26, **−34**
The rule is subtract 8 each time.
d) 28, **24**, **20**, 16, 12
The rule is subtract 4 each time.

3 39, **35**, **31**, **27**, **23**
Rule: **subtract 4**

4 a) The number decreases by 5 each day:
35, **30**, **25**, **20**, **15**
b) Extending the sequence gives:
35, 30, 25, 20, 15, 10, 5, 0
So the 8th term is 0 and
the box is empty at the end of day **8**.

5 a)

Pattern Number	1	2	3	4	5
Number of Acorns	**3**	**5**	**7**	**9**	**11**

b) The rule for the sequence is that you add 2 each time.
Extending the sequence gives:
3, 5, 7, 9, 11, 13, 15, 17, 19, 21
So in the 10th pattern, the number of acorns will be **21**.

6 a) 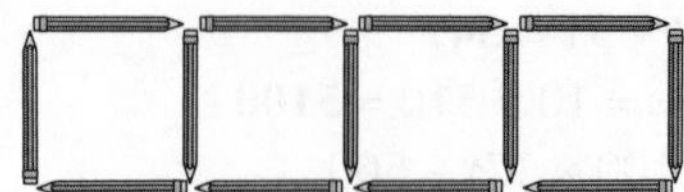

b) The rule for the sequence is that you add 3 each time.
Extending the sequence gives: 4, 7, 10, 13, 16, 19, 22
So to make the 7th pattern, Maj uses **22 pencils**.

Pages 48-49 — Coordinates

1 (7, 8) = **P** (2, 2) = **O** (11, 1) = **L** (5, 6) = **L** (5, 10) = **Y**
The x-coordinate (↔) is the first value and the y-coordinate (↕) is the second value.

2 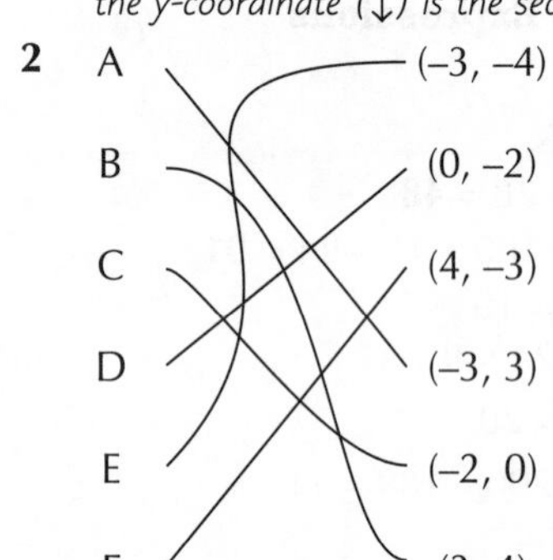

3 **(10, 5)** and **(4, 2)**

4 ☑ (1, 2) & (1, 3)
☑ (–6, 2) & (–6, 1)
☑ (–3, –3) & (–3, 3)
The pairs with the same x-coordinate lie on the same vertical line.

5 a) **(–2, 2)**

b) 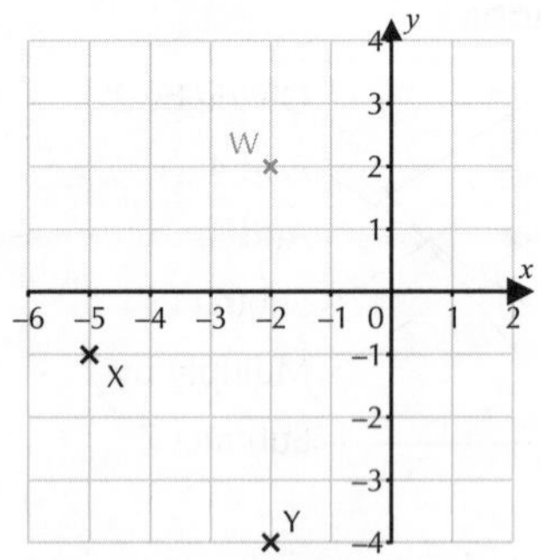

c) Draw in the lines connecting W to X and X to Y.
To make this into a square, the fourth corner must be the point labelled Z on the diagram below.

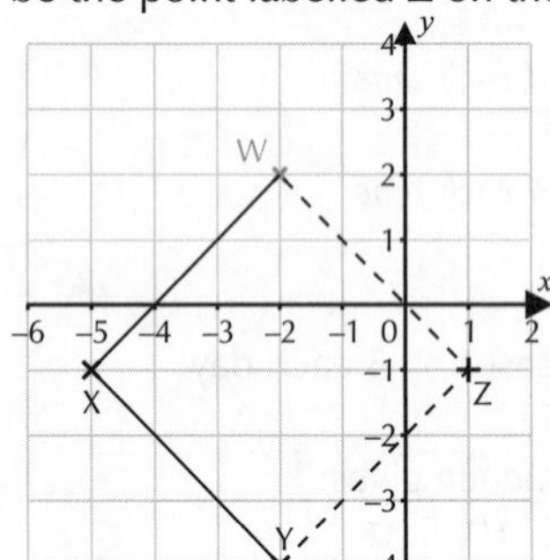

The coordinates of the fourth vertex are **(1, –1)**.

6 a) 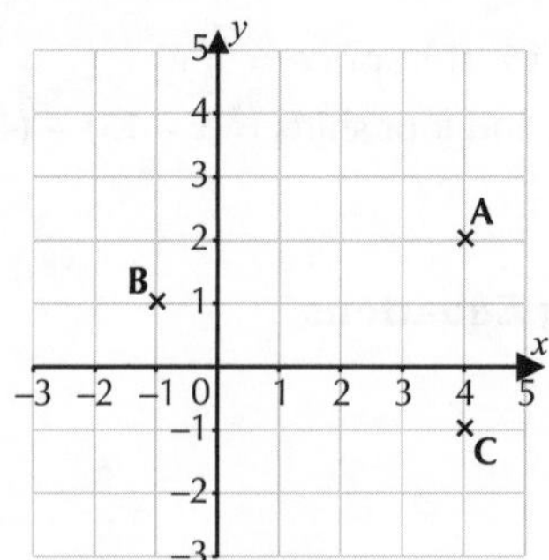

b) (i) 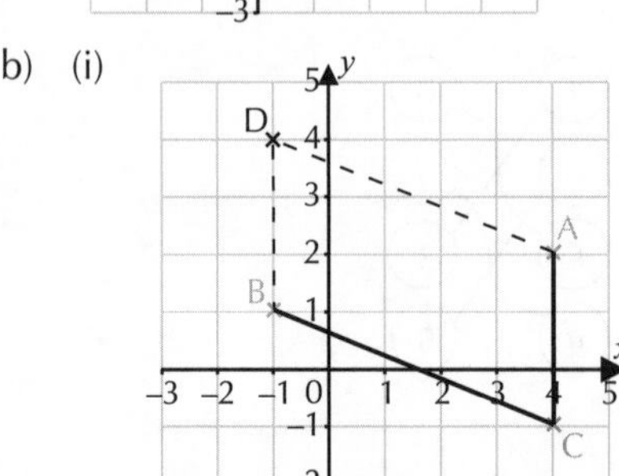

(ii) The coordinates of D are **(–1, 4)**.

Pages 50-51 — Review Exercise

1 a) **$3y$ *[1 mark]*** b) **$3x^2y$ *[1 mark]***

2 a) $x = 14 \div 7 =$ **2** ***[1 mark]***
b) $x = 81 - 9 =$ **72** ***[1 mark]***
c) $7x = 35$
$x = 35 \div 7 =$ **5** ***[1 mark]***
d) $25x = 150$
$x = 150 \div 25 =$ **6** ***[1 mark]***

3 a) $3x - 7 = 17$
$3x = 24$ ***[1 mark]***
$x = 8$ *[1 mark]*
[2 marks available in total — as above]

b) $7x = 44 - 4x$
$7x + 4x = 44$
$11x = 44$ ***[1 mark]***
$x = 4$ *[1 mark]*
[2 marks available in total — as above]

4 a) $(7 \times 4) + 8 = 28 + 8 =$ **36** ***[1 mark]***
b) $3 - (4 \times 3) = 3 - 12 =$ **–9** ***[1 mark]***
c) $-7 - (8 \times 2) + (2 \times 3) = -7 - 16 + 6$ ***[1 mark]***
$=$ **–17** ***[1 mark]***
[2 marks available in total — as above]

5 $C = (2 \times 4) + 15 = 8 + 15 =$ **£23** ***[1 mark]***

6 a) **$S = 4$ *[1 mark]*** E.g. the term-to-term rule is 'add 6' and $-2 + 6 = 4$ ***[1 mark]***.
[2 marks available in total — as above]

b) **No** ***[1 mark]*** — e.g. the first sequence has **even terms**, the second sequence has **odd terms** ***[1 mark]***.
[2 marks available in total — as above]

7 a) To get the next pattern in the sequence, 3 doughnuts are added. So the next two patterns will look like this:

[2 marks available — 1 mark for each pattern]

b) 3 doughnuts are added in each pattern, so the sequence is 2, 5, 8, 11, 14, 17, 20.... So the 7th pattern has **20 doughnuts**. ***[1 mark]***

8 a) **(–1, 2)** ***[1 mark]***

b) See below.
[2 marks available — 2 marks for all three coordinates correctly drawn, otherwise 1 mark for two coordinates correctly drawn]

c) Join up the coordinates.

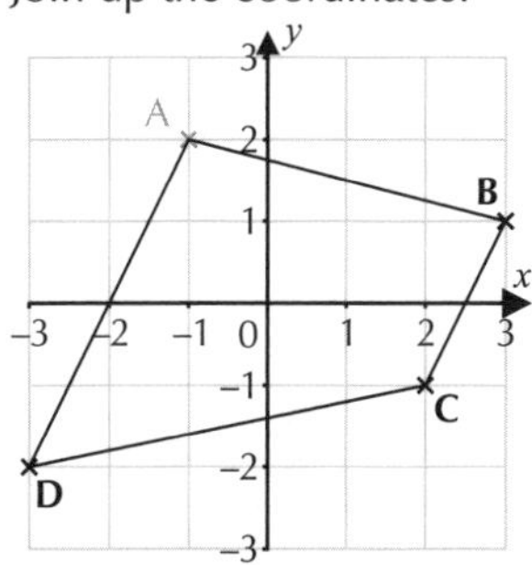

AD and BC are parallel (but AB and CD aren't), so the shape is a **trapezium**. ***[1 mark]***

Section Four — Geometry

Page 52 — Before you Start

1 a) **Rectangle** b) **Pentagon** c) **Parallelogram**
Rectangles and parallelograms are both 'quadrilaterals', but you need to give their specific names if you're asked what they're called.

2 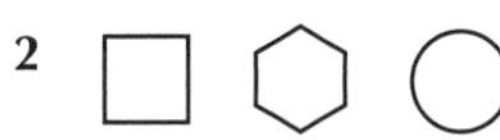

3 **7 cm**

4

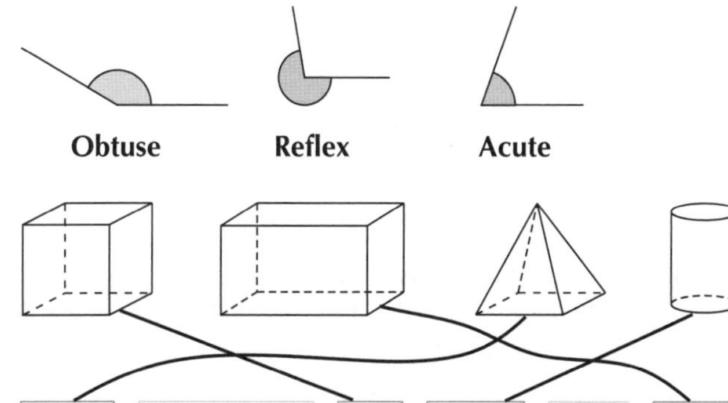

Obtuse **Reflex** **Acute**

5

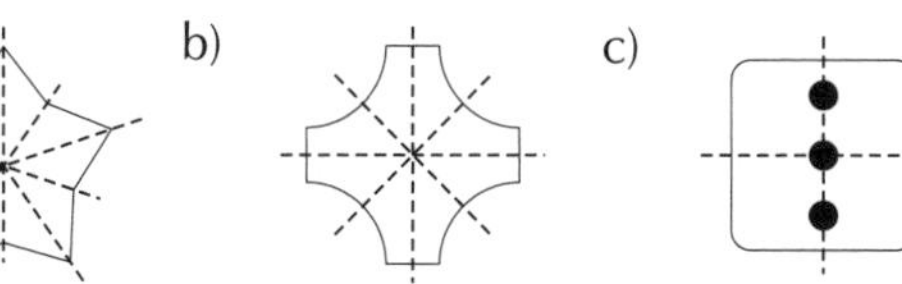

Pyramid Triangular Prism Cube Cylinder Sphere Cuboid

Page 53 — Symmetry

1 a) b) c)

2

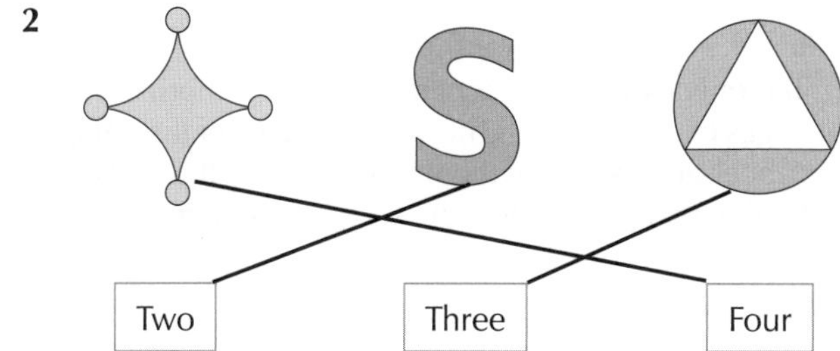

3

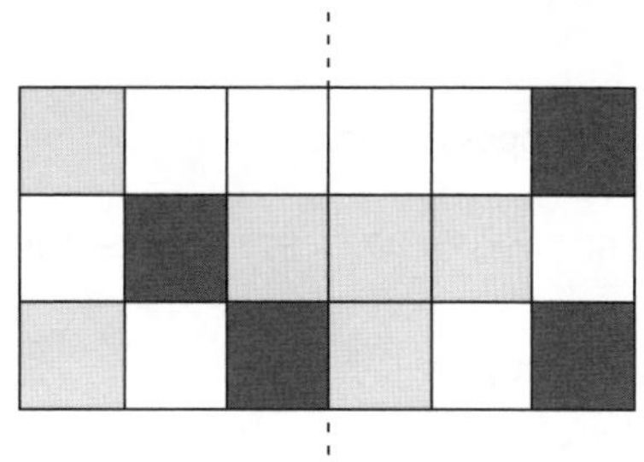

Page 54 — Properties of Triangles

1 a)

b) **4**
Ms. Gular's body and legs are right-angled triangles.

c) **Equilateral**

Equilateral triangles (like Ms. Gular's head) are sometimes thought of as a type of isosceles triangle — so it's okay if you shaded her head for part a) as well.

2 a) **equilateral** b) **zero**
c) **sometimes** d) **impossible**

3 a)

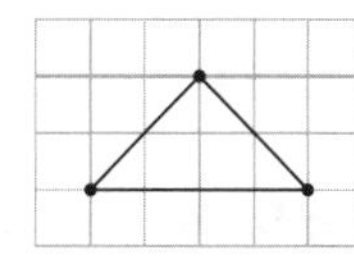

b) E.g.

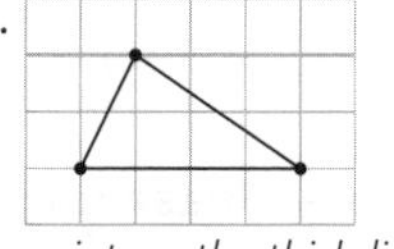

Any point on the thick line except the answer to part a) works.

Page 55 — Properties of Quadrilaterals

1 a) **Square**, **Rectangle**, **Rhombus**, **Parallelogram**
b) **Square**, **Rhombus, Kite**
c) **Kite**, **Trapezium**

2 ✓ It has four sides of equal length.
✓ It has two lines of symmetry.
✓ It has two pairs of equal angles.

3 a)

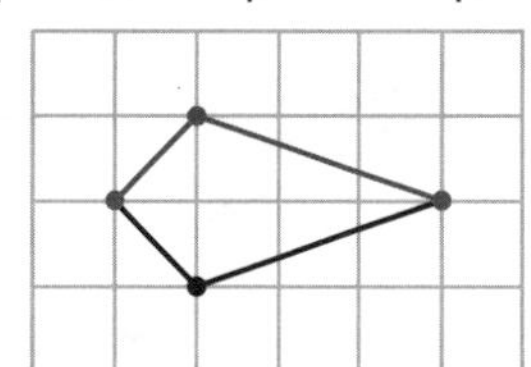

b) E.g.

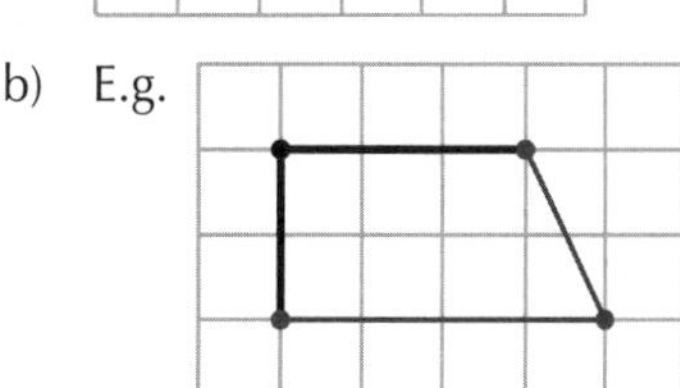

Any point will work so long as it creates a pair of parallel sides.

Page 56 — Angle Rules

1 *For this question, use the rules that angles on a line add up to 180° and angles around a point add up to 360°.*

a) $a = 180° - 125° =$ **55°**
b) $b = 360° - 220° =$ **140°**
c) $c = 360° - 90° - 150° =$ **120°**

2 *For this question, use the rule that vertically opposite angles are equal.*

a) $j =$ **100°**
b) $m =$ **120°**, $n =$ **60°**
c) $r =$ **95°**, $s = 180° - 95° =$ **85°**, $t = s =$ **85°**

3 A: 23°
B: 90° – 43° = 47°
C: 57° (using vertically opposite angles)
D: 180° – 86° = 94°
So the angle in E is 360° – 23° – 47° – 57° – 94° = **139°**.

Page 57 — Angles in Triangles

For these questions, use that angles in a triangle add up to 180°.

1 a) $w = 180° – 90° – 30° =$ **60°**
b) $x = 180° – 84° – 50° =$ **46°**
c) $180° – 110° = 70°$, $y = z = 70° ÷ 2 =$ **35°**
The triangle is isosceles, so y is equal to z.

2 a) $x = 180° – 75° – 40° =$ **65°**
$y = x =$ **65°**
b) Angles on a straight line add up to 180°, so the unmarked angle in the triangle is 180° – 60° = 120°. So $x = 180° – 120° – 25° =$ **35°**.

3 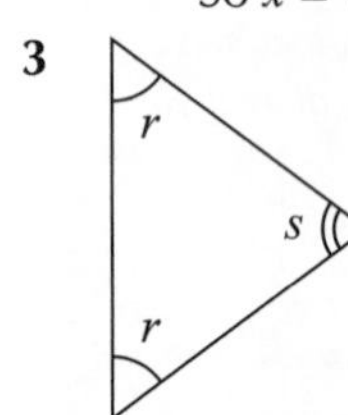

First work out the angle marked s in this diagram. There are 5 triangles in the logo and they all meet at a point, so $5 \times s = 360°$
$\Rightarrow s = 360° ÷ 5 = 72°$.
Angles in a triangle add up to 180°, so $2r + 72° = 180°$
$\Rightarrow r = (180° – 72°) ÷ 2 =$ **54°**.

Page 58 — Measuring and Drawing Lines and Angles

1 $p =$ **60°**, $q =$ **110°**, $r =$ **20°**

2 a) 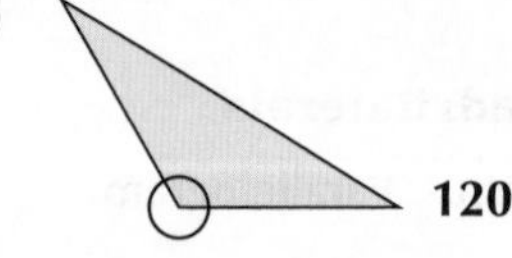

b) 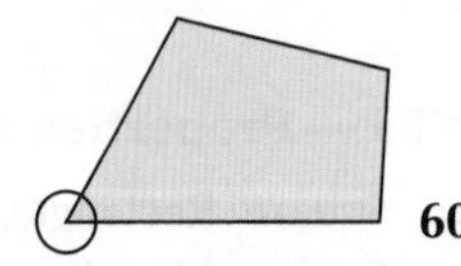

3 215° is a reflex angle, but your protractor only measures angles up to 180°. Work out the other angle around the point B and measure this instead: 360° – 215° = 145°.

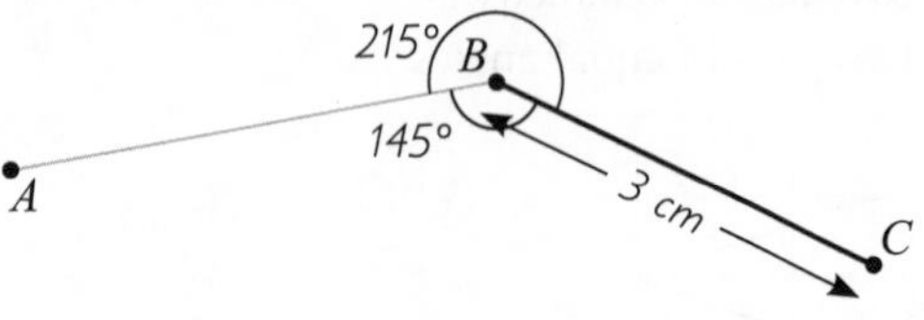

4 a) 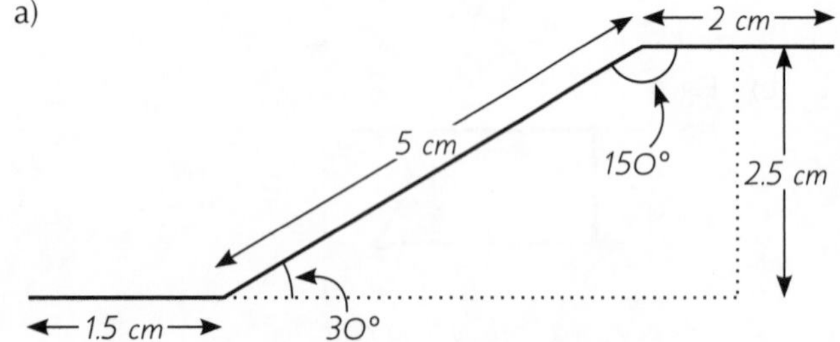

b) **2.5 cm** (see above)
Allow answers between 2.3 cm and 2.7 cm.

Page 59 — Constructing Triangles

1 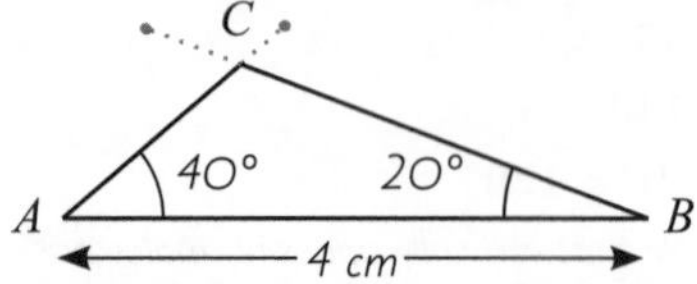

2 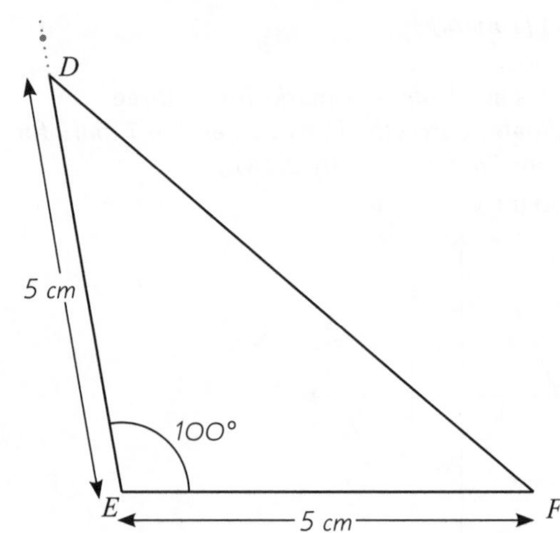

3 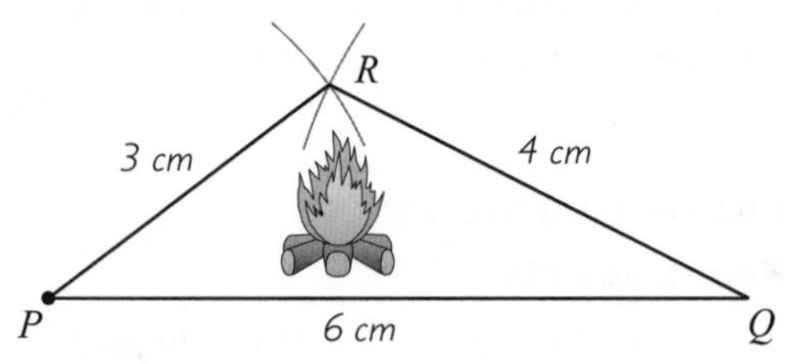

Pages 60-61 — Perimeter

1 a) 4 + 4 + 4 + 4 = **16 m** b) 3 + 8 + 3 + 8 = **22 m**
c) 2.5 + 3.5 + 5 = **11 m**

2 a) 3 × 7 = **21 m** b) 5 × 2 = **10 m**
Since the shapes are regular, all the sides are the same length.

3 2 + 4 + 1 + 3 + 1 + 1 = **12 cm**

4 a) $x = 21 – 2 – 5 – 8 =$ **6 m**
b) The triangle is isosceles, so the unlabelled side also has a length of y. So $25 = 2y + 9$.
$y = (25 – 9) ÷ 2 = 16 ÷ 2 =$ **8 m**

5 a) 7 + 6 + 12 + 6 + 7 = **38 m**
b) The missing lengths are 3 m, 3 m and 8 – 3 – 4 = 1 m. So the perimeter is 8 + 3 + 3 + 3 + 4 + 3 + 1 + 3 = **28 m**.

6 a) 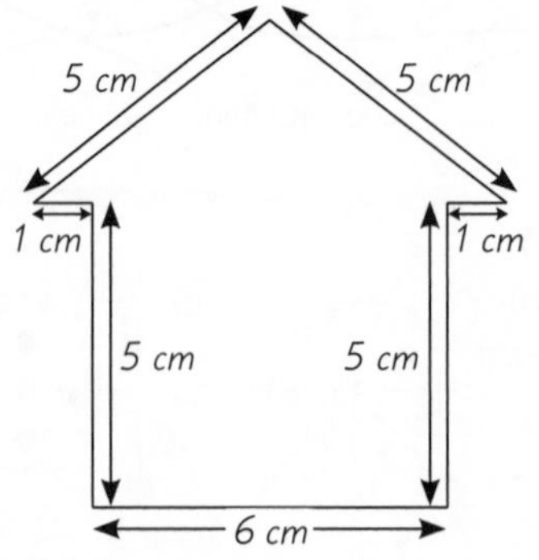

6 + 5 + 1 + 5 + 5 + 1 + 5 = **28 cm**.
b) The only extra perimeter comes from the horizontal edges of the garage. (The vertical edges of the garage cancel out, as one of them is attached to the house.) So the total perimeter is 28 + 4 + 4 = **36 cm**.

Pages 62-63 — Area

1 The shape is made up of 6 full squares and 4 half squares. So the area is 6 × 1 + 4 × 0.5 = 6 + 2 = **8 cm²**.

2 a) 6 × 6 = **36 m²** b) 4 × 7 = **28 m²**
c) E.g. split the shape into two rectangles — one with dimensions 6 cm by 4 cm and one with dimensions 3 cm by 4 cm. Then the area of the shape is (6 × 4) + (3 × 4) = **36 m²**.

3 a) $\frac{1}{2} \times 6 \times 5 =$ **15 m²**

b) $\frac{1}{2} \times 6 \times 4 =$ **12 m²**

c) $\frac{1}{2} \times 8 \times 7 =$ **28 m²**

4 a) $x = \sqrt{64} =$ **8 m** b) $y = 64 \div 16 =$ **4 m**

5 Divide the shape in two pieces as shown below.

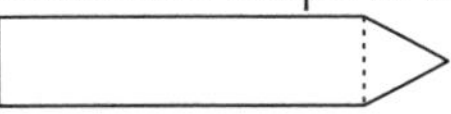

The rectangle has an area of $35 \times 10 = 350$ cm².
The triangle has a height of $45 - 35 = 10$ cm,
so it has an area of $\frac{1}{2} \times 10 \times 10 = 50$ cm².
So the total area is $350 + 50 =$ **400 cm²**.

6 **No**. The height of the envelope is $176 \div 16 = 11$ cm, which is smaller than the lengths of the sides of the paper.

7 The height of the right-angled piece is equal to the side length, l, of the equilateral piece.

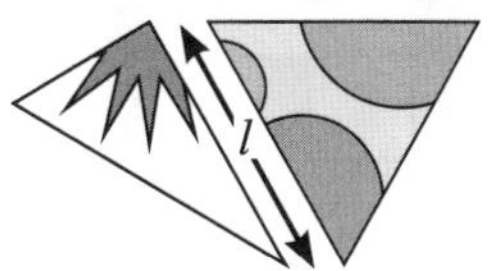

Using the given area of the equilateral piece,
$1560 = \frac{1}{2} \times 52 \times l$, so $1560 = 26l$. $l = 1560 \div 26 = 60$ cm.
So the area of the right-angled triangle is
$\frac{1}{2} \times 30 \times l = \frac{1}{2} \times 30 \times 60 = 900$ cm².
So the area of the whole rug is
$(4 \times 1560) + (4 \times 900) =$ **9840 cm²**.

Page 64 — Reflection

1

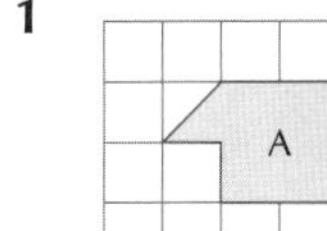

2 a)

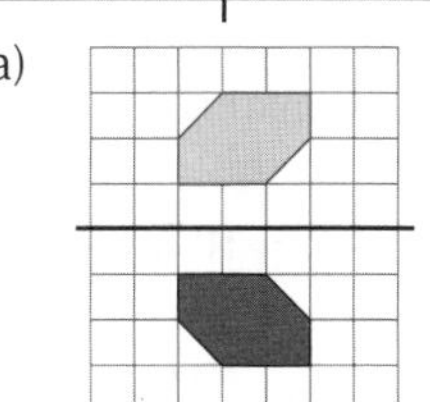

b)

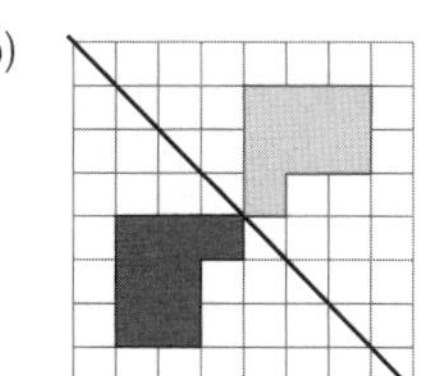

3 a) *C*

b)

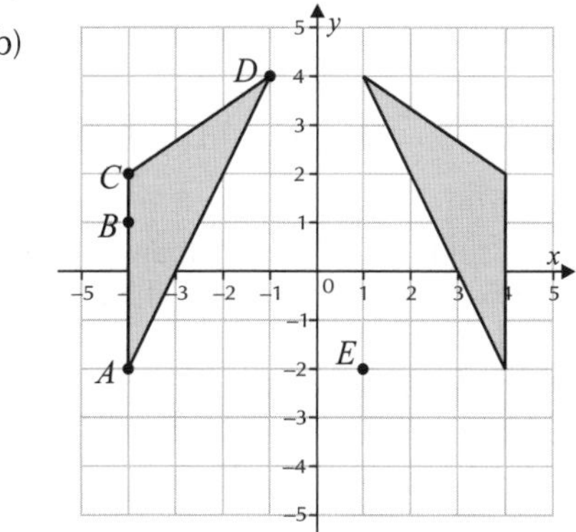

c) Reflecting E in the x-axis takes you to (1, 2).
Then reflecting in the y-axis takes you to **(–1, 2)**.

Page 65 — 3D Shapes

1 a) **Cone** b) **Tetrahedron** c) **Sphere**
You could also write triangular-based pyramid for part b).

2

Name	Cube	**Triangular Prism**	Square-based Pyramid	Pentagonal Prism
Faces	**6**	**5**	**5**	**7**
Vertices	8	**6**	**5**	**10**
Edges	**12**	9	**8**	**15**

3

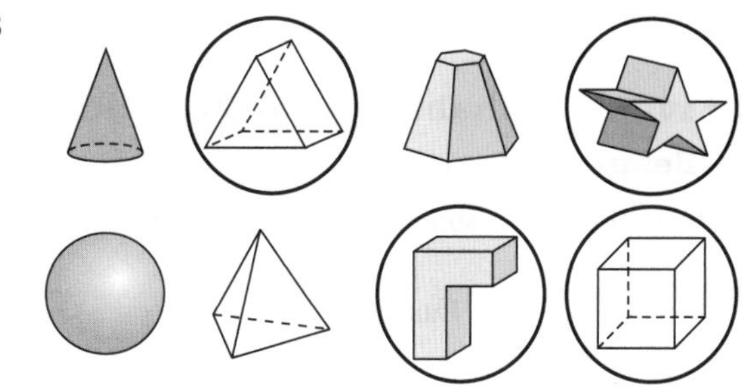

Page 66 — Volume

1 a) $5 \times 1 =$ **5 cm³** b) $7 \times 1 =$ **7 cm³**
Count the number of blocks and multiply by their volume of 1 cm³.

2 a) $5 \times 5 \times 5 =$ **125 cm³** b) $4 \times 8 \times 3 =$ **96 m³**

3 a) $108 \div 4 =$ **27 cm³**

b) $27 = 3 \times 3 \times 3$, so the height of each cube is 3 cm.
So the height of the tower is $4 \times 3 =$ **12 cm**.

Pages 67-68 — Review Exercise

1 a) (i) **2 *[1 mark]*** — as shown below.

(ii) **2 *[1 mark]***

b)

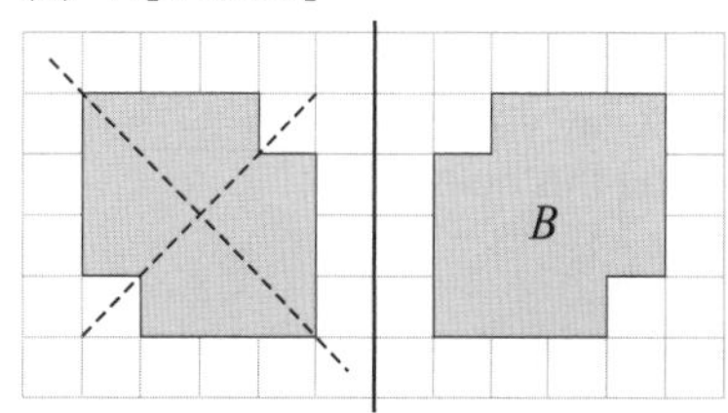

[1 mark]

2 a) (i) The two missing lengths are $12 - 7 = 5$ m and $4 - 2 = 2$ m. So the perimeter is $2 + 5 + 2 + 7 + 4 + 12 =$ **32 m**. ***[1 mark]***

(ii) $(5 \times 2) + (7 \times 4) = 10 + 28 =$ **38 m²**
[2 marks available — 1 mark for a correct method, 1 mark for the correct answer]

b) Using the areas calculated in part a),
the volume is $(1 \times 10) + (2 \times 28) =$ **66 m³**.
[2 marks available — 1 mark for a correct method, 1 mark for the correct answer]

3 a) **Trapezium** ***[1 mark]***

b) (i) $h =$ **4 cm** ***[1 mark]***

(ii) The trapezium is a composite shape made up of a triangle and a rectangle.
The area of the rectangle is $1 \times 4 = 4$ cm².
The area of the triangle is $\frac{1}{2} \times 4 \times 4 = 8$ cm².
So the trapezium has an area of $4 + 8 =$ **12 cm²**.
[2 marks available — 1 mark for a correct method, 1 mark for the correct answer]

c) $p =$ **45°** ***[1 mark]***

d) The prism has **6** faces, **8** vertices and **12** edges.
[2 marks available — 2 marks for all three values correct, otherwise 1 mark for two correct]

4 a) **Isosceles** ***[1 mark]***

b) Since the triangle is isosceles, there are two 35° angles. So x = 180° – (35° × 2) = **110°**.
[2 marks available — 1 mark for knowing that there are two 35° angles, 1 mark for the correct answer]

c) Area = 9 = $\frac{1}{2}$ × b × h, so b × h = 9 × 2 = 18.
So b and h can be any two positive whole numbers that multiply to give 18:
2 cm and **9** cm, **3** cm and **6** cm, **1** cm and **18** cm
[2 marks available — 1 mark for each correct pair]

Section Five — Probability and Statistics

Page 69 — Before you Start

1 **☑ A baby will be born somewhere in the world today.**

2 **Evens**

3 a) **2450** b) **Thursday**

4 **30 °C, 40 °C**

Pages 70-71 — Probability

1

There will be fewer than 30 days in February.	Certain
You will find a giraffe in your street tomorrow.	Unlikely
It will rain while you're outside at some point in the next year.	Likely
You will pick a red ball from a bag containing only 5 red and 5 blue balls.	Evens
You will develop X-ray vision by correctly answering this question.	Impossible

2
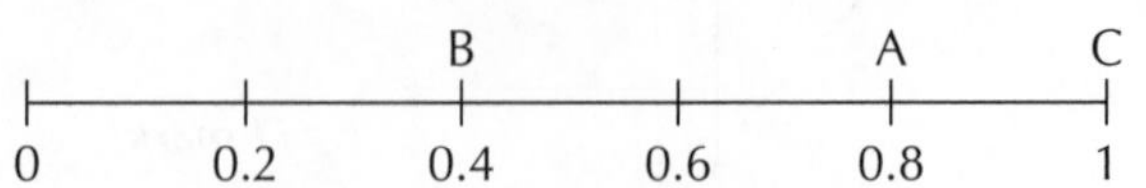

a) Four out of five people got the bus, so the probability is $\frac{4}{5}$ = **0.8**.

b) Two out of five people got on a bus that was late, so the probability is $\frac{2}{5}$ = **0.4**.

c) All of the people arrived on time, so the probability is $\frac{5}{5}$ = **1**.

3 The probability of A is $\frac{1}{2}$, the probability of B is $\frac{1}{6}$ and the probability of C is 0 (since it's impossible for the dice to land on 7). So the order is **C**, **B**, **A**.

4 a) There are 10 possible tickets and only one numbered 6, so the probability that the ticket is 6 is $\mathbf{\frac{1}{10}}$.

b) There are 5 even-numbered tickets, so the probability is $\frac{5}{10}$ = $\mathbf{\frac{1}{2}}$.

c) There are 2 odd-numbered tickets less than 5, so the probability is $\frac{2}{10}$ = $\mathbf{\frac{1}{5}}$.

5 a) P(no walk) = 1 – P(walk) = 1 – 0.2 = **0.8**

b) Probabilities must add up to 1:
P(beach) + P(park) + P(river) = 1
⇒ 0.4 + 0.1 + P(river) = 1
⇒ P(river) = 1 – 0.4 – 0.1 = **0.5**

6 a) 10 + 25 = 35 of the jars contain either apricot or strawberry jam, so the probability is $\frac{35}{80}$ = $\mathbf{\frac{7}{16}}$.

b) 80 – 10 = 70 of the jars don't contain apricot jam, so the probability is $\frac{70}{80}$ = $\mathbf{\frac{7}{8}}$.

c) None of the jars contain blackberry jam, so the probability is **0**.

Pages 72-74 — Tables, Bar Charts and Pictograms

1 a) **Davood**

b) 555 + 189 + 464 + 651 + 548 = **2407 g**

c) 555 – 189 = **366 g**

2 a)
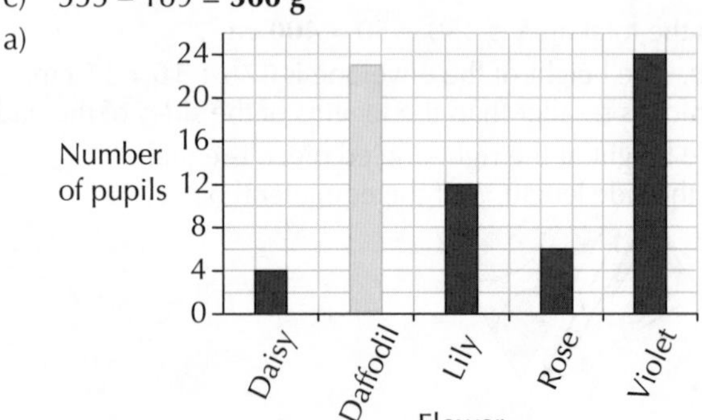

b) **23**

3 a)

Suit	♣	♠	♦	♥
Tally	卌 |||	||||	||	||||
Frequency	**8**	**4**	**2**	**4**

b) There are 4 hearts and 8 + 4 + 2 + 4 = 18 cards in total, so the fraction is $\frac{4}{18}$ = $\mathbf{\frac{2}{9}}$.

4 a) 1 symbol represents 4 houses, so 8 houses is represented by 2 symbols.

Price	
£100 000-£149 999	☐ ☐

b) The row for 'less than £100 000' contains 2 full symbols and 1 half-symbol, so this represents (2 × 4) + ($\frac{1}{2}$ × 4) = 8 + 2 = **10 houses**.

c) In the price range £200 000-£249 999, there are 4 full symbols and 1 half-symbol, so (4 × 4) + ($\frac{1}{2}$ × 4) = 16 + 2 = 18 houses were sold.
In the price range £250 000 or more, there is 1 three-quarter-symbol, so $\frac{3}{4}$ × 4 = 3 houses were sold. So 18 + 3 = 21 were sold for £200 000 or more. $\frac{21}{50}$ = $\frac{42}{100}$ = **42%**

5 a) There were more sightings in the UK than in Denmark when the darker bar is taller than the lighter one. This happens in **1 year** (2018).

b) Total sightings in the UK since 2016: 2 + 5 + 6 = 13
Total sightings in Denmark since 2016: 8 + 5 + 1 = 14
So there was 14 – 13 = **1 more sighting**.

c) E.g.

Key: ○ = 2 snowmen

Number of sightings	
2013	○
2014	○ ○ ◖
2015	◖
2016	○
2017	○ ○ ◖
2018	○ ○ ○

d) E.g. **No** — the number of sightings in Denmark is increasing from 2013 to 2015, but decreasing from 2016 onwards.

Pages 75-76 — Pie Charts

1 a) The 'pie charts' sector takes up half of the pie chart, so it represents **50%** of the mathematicians.

b) A quarter of the mathematicians said bar charts, so this is 56 ÷ 4 = **14 mathematicians**.

2 a) **Pearl**

b) 15 rubies are represented by 120°.
120° is one third of 360°, so 15 rubies must be one third of the total number of gems.
So there are 3 × 15 = **45 gems** in total.

3 There are 60 – 15 – 25 = 20 yellow squares.
One square is represented by 360° ÷ 60 = 6°.

Colour	Number of squares	Angle
Red	15	15 × 6° = **90°**
Blue	**25**	25 × 6° = **150°**
Yellow	**20**	20 × 6° = **120°**

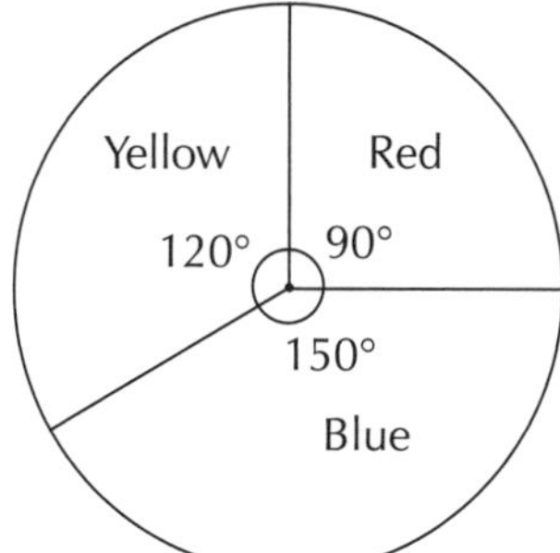

4 You only know the proportion of people cast in three plays, but you don't know how many people the pie chart represents.

5 a) (i) **60°** (ii) $\frac{60°}{360°} = \mathbf{\frac{1}{6}}$

b) (i) Use your answer to a) (ii).
Old area of industry district = 120 × $\frac{1}{6}$ = 20 km²
New area of industry district = 2 × 20 = **40 km²**

(ii) $\frac{40}{180}$ × 360° = **80°**

Pages 77-78 — Mean, Median, Mode and Range

1 a) The number which occurs the most often is **3**.

b) (i) **2, 3, 3, 4, 5, 6, 7** (ii) 7 – 2 = **5**
(iii) The median is in the middle: **4**

2 a) 32 + 40 + 25 + 12 + 9 + 48 + 27 + 15 = **208**

b) There are 8 values, so mean = 208 ÷ 8 = **26**

3 a) 4 – 1 = **3**

b) 1, 1, 1, 2, 3, 4
Mode = 1
The median is half-way between 1 and 2, so it's 1.5.
Mean = (1 + 1 + 1 + 2 + 3 + 4) ÷ 6 = 12 ÷ 6 = 2
(i) The **mean** of the numbers is 2.
(ii) The **median** of the numbers is 1.5.

4 a) Total = 3.2 + 6.8 + 7.2 + 5.3 + 4.4 + 5.5 = 32.4 g
Mean = 32.4 ÷ 6 = **5.4 g**

b) (i) 7.2 – 3.2 = **4 g**
(ii) Using the actual mass would make the range smaller since you're subtracting a bigger number.

5 a) Write the times in order (converting 1 hour to 60 minutes): 15, 26, 32, 45, 60
So the median is **32 minutes**.

b) (i) Total = 15 + 26 + 32 + 45 + 60 = 178 minutes
Mean = 178 ÷ 5 = 35.6 = **36 minutes** (to the nearest minute)

(ii) On average, it took the second group longer than it took the first group.
Answer this question by comparing the means — 40 minutes is greater than 36 minutes.

Pages 79-80 — Review Exercise

1 a) 1 symbol represents 4 phones. One bar of signal is represented by 2 full symbols and 1 half-symbol, so this is (2 × 4) + ($\frac{1}{2}$ × 4) = 8 + 2 = **10 phones**. ***[1 mark]***

b) In the whole diagram, there are:
8 full symbols (8 × 4 = 32 phones),
1 three-quarter symbol (1 × $\frac{3}{4}$ × 4 = 3 phones),
2 half-symbols (2 × $\frac{1}{2}$ × 4 = 4 phones) and
1 quarter symbol (1 × $\frac{1}{4}$ × 4 = 1 phone).
So in total, there are 32 + 3 + 4 + 1 = 40 phones.
So the probability is $\frac{10}{40}$ = 0.25.

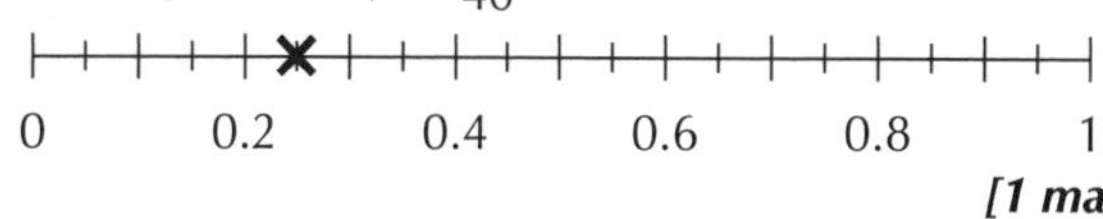

[1 mark]

2 a) (i) Put the numbers in order:
6, 8, 8, 9, 9, 10, 10, 12
So the median is **9**. ***[1 mark]***

(ii) Total = 6 + 8 + 8 + 9 + 9 + 10 + 10 + 12
= 72 ***[1 mark]***
Mean = 72 ÷ 8 = **9** ***[1 mark]***
[2 marks available in total — as above]

b) There are 115 + 98 + 51 = 264 visitors ***[1 mark]*** with a shoe size greater than 9. So the fraction of visitors is $\frac{264}{1056} = \mathbf{\frac{1}{4}}$ ***[1 mark]***.

3 a) Number of green sheep = 72 ÷ 2 = 36
Number of yellow sheep = 72 – 36 – 16 = 20 ***[1 mark]***
So the probability is $\frac{20}{72} = \mathbf{\frac{5}{18}}$. ***[1 mark]***
[2 marks available in total — as above]

b) 1 sheep is represented by 360° ÷ 72 = 5°.
So 36 green sheep are represented by 5 × 36 = 180°, 16 red sheep by 5 × 16 = 80° and 20 yellow sheep by 5 × 20 = 100°.

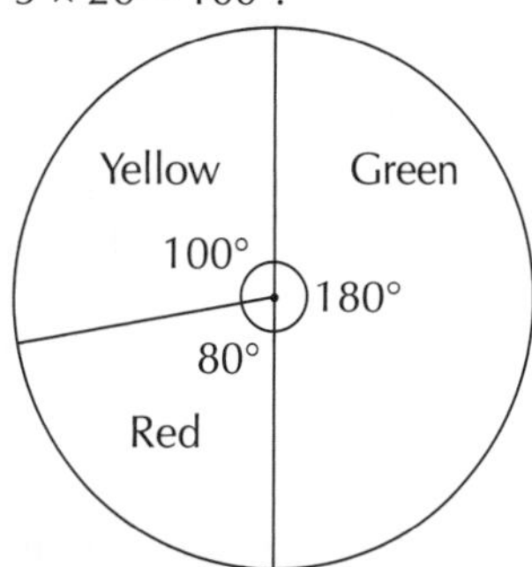

[3 marks available — 1 mark drawing the green sector correctly, 1 mark for working out the angle of the yellow or red sector, 1 mark for the completely correct pie chart]

4 a) There were 33 loaves and 22 pies sold, so that's 33 – 22 = **11 fewer pies**. ***[1 mark]***

b) There were 10 biscuits sold. 10 is not a multiple of 4, so they can't all have been sold in packs of 4. ***[1 mark]***

c) Range = greatest number – lowest number
12 = 52 – lowest number
So lowest number = 52 – 12 = **40** ***[1 mark]***

Topic Map

There's a whole bunch of maths to learn at Key Stage 3 — and different schools teach the content in different orders. This table shows you where we introduce each of the topics from the curriculum.

	Year 7 Workbook	Year 8 Workbook	Year 9 Workbook
Section One — Number	**Place value and ordering numbers**		
	Addition and subtraction — whole numbers, decimals	**Addition and subtraction —** harder decimals, negative numbers	**Solving number problems —** using non-calculator arithmetic
	Multiplication and division — powers of 10, whole numbers	**Multiplication and division —** decimals, negative numbers	
	Negative numbers — ordering, simple addition	**Negative numbers —** harder calculations	
	BODMAS — brackets, division, multiplication, addition, subtraction	**BODMAS —** brackets, powers and roots, division, multiplication, addition, subtraction	
	Inverse operations		
	Rounding — to the nearest 10, 100, 1000, etc., to the nearest whole number	**Rounding —** decimal places, significant figures	**Rounding —** rounding errors, inequality notation
	Estimating — by rounding to whole numbers or to the nearest 10, 100, 1000, etc.	**Estimating —** by rounding to 1 significant figure	**Estimating —** solving problems by rounding to specified accuracy
	Powers and roots — squares, square roots, cubes, cube roots	**Powers and roots —** higher powers, powers of 10, approximating roots	**Power and roots —** power laws, negative powers
			Standard form
	Multiples and LCM		
	Factors and HCF		
	Prime numbers — identifying primes	**Prime factorisation —** factor trees, product notation	**Prime factorisation —** using prime factors to find e.g. LCM, HCF, squares, roots
Section Two — Proportions and Units	**Fraction basics —** equivalent fractions, ordering fractions, mixed numbers, improper fractions		**Solving fraction problems**
	Adding and subtracting fractions — denominators with a common factor	**Adding and subtracting fractions —** denominators with no common factors	
	Multiplying fractions — by whole numbers	**Multiplying fractions —** by other fractions	
		Dividing fractions	
	Fractions, decimals, percentages — simple converting without a calculator	**Fractions, decimals, percentages —** harder converting, comparing proportions	
	Percentages of amounts — with and without a calculator	**Percentages of amounts —** solving harder problems	
		Percentage change — finding new amounts, finding the original amount	**Percentage change —** finding the percentage change, simple interest, harder problems
	Ratios — introducing ratio notation, simplifying ratios	**Ratios —** harder simplifying, writing in the form $1:n$, solving ratio problems	**Ratios —** decimals, mixed units, harder ratio problems
	Proportion — comparing amounts using fractions, percentages and ratios	**Proportion —** scaling up and down	**Proportion —** direct and inverse proportion, harder scaling problems, algebra and graphs
	Time — converting between the 12- and 24-hour clock, units of time, timetables		
		Compound measures — speed problems	**Compound measures —** harder speed problems, density problems, best buy problems
	Units — using metric units, converting between metric units	**Units —** converting between metric and imperial units	**Units —** converting compound units, including areas and volumes
		Scales and scale drawings — converting and drawing using simple scales	**Scales and scale drawings —** scales given as ratios

M7W32